MOLLUSKS

PAUL BARTSCH

Sometime Curator, Division of Mollusks
United States National Museum

DOVER PUBLICATIONS, INC.
NEW YORK

Published in Canada by General Publishing Company, Ltd.,
30 Lesmill Road, Don Mills, Toronto, Ontario.

Published in the United Kingdom by Constable and Company, Ltd.,
10 Orange Street, London WC 2.

This Dover edition, first published in 1968, is an unabridged republication
of Part III, "Mollusks," from *Shelled Invertebrates of the Past and Present, with
Chapters on Geological History*, by Ray S. Bassler, Charles E. Resser, Waldo L.
Schmitt and Paul Bartsch, as published in 1934 by the Smithsonian Institution
as Volume 10 of the Smithsonian Institution Series.

International Standard Book Number: 0–486–21899–6
Library of Congress Catalog Card Number: 68–12914

Manufactured in the United States of America

Dover Publications, Inc.
180 Varick Street
New York, N. Y. 10014

CONTENTS

LIST OF ILLUSTRATIONS

COLOR PLATES

(Between pages 84 and 85)

HALFTONE PLATES

MOLLUSKS

LIST OF ILLUSTRATIONS

CHAPTER I

THE RANKING INVERTEBRATES

EVERY specialist in natural history feels that his own specialty leads all others in interest and even in significance in the scheme of nature. Such partiality constitutes both the weakness and the strength of scientists: weakness because it is an admission of their liability to human error, for certainly they can not all be right; and strength because the belief spurs them to the effort that only the service of the "most important" can call forth. It should occasion no surprise, therefore, if I begin this paper with the claim that the Mollusca rank at the top of all invertebrate life in complexity of organization and intelligence, as they certainly do in size, ferocity, and speed of movement; and that in many of these particulars they surpass groups of the lower Chordata (the animal subkingdom distinguished by the possession of a notochord, or incipient backbone).

So bald a claim probably sticks in the crop even of the layman who makes a mental comparison of the mollusks he knows best—the oyster and the snail—with the colony-forming insects—bees and ants—which have such a high state of social organization and seeming intelligence. On the other hand the claim will probably be accepted, however reluctantly, even by the specialist, who remembers that the octopus and squid, also, are mollusks and compares them with the remainder of the invertebrate world. For it is this upper class of mollusks which hitches the phylum to the top rung of the invertebrate ladder.

At the risk of being technical we can adduce structural evidence to justify our claim. The ten classes of animals which make up the subkingdom Chordata are held together by only a few common characters, namely, a notochord (the precursor of the spinal column); a neurocoele (the tube in the center of the spinal chord); and a perforated pharynx. Now the perforated pharynx is certainly nothing more than the modified gill of the Mollusca, so that here we have one basic character that ties that subkingdom to the Chordata. A much better claim of the Mollusca to equality with the latter subkingdom, however, is based on the fact that the brain of the octopus (and of all the other members of the class Cephalopoda) is like that of the higher vertebrates including man in one important character: the same complex arrangement of the innervation of the eye occurs in both. This arrangement is called the optic chiasma; in animals possessing it, the optic nerve from the right eye leads not only to the right cerebrum but also to the left; likewise the nerve of the left eye leads to both the left and right cerebrums. It is this high specialization of the brain that carries the cephalopods far beyond even the lower chordates in development.

So much for the right of Mollusca to our respect as "almost equals." The many qualities of all members of the phylum and especially of the Cephalopoda will speak better for themselves than we can speak for them. Among the invertebrates their nearest relatives are the Arthropoda, the subkingdom that includes the crustaceans, insects, spiders, centipedes, and similar forms. Mollusks differ from arthropods in lacking jointed appendages, such as legs and antennae. They are further distinctive in that they go through a veliger larval, or embryonic, stage, a phase of development not found in any animals of lower rank than the subkingdom Mollusca. This will be more fully dealt with in our chapter on the Pelecypoda.

After this brief discussion of relationships we may define a mollusk as a soft-bodied, unsegmented animal enveloped by a mantle, or soft integument, which secretes the protective shell whenever this is present. It is the shell

PLATE 1

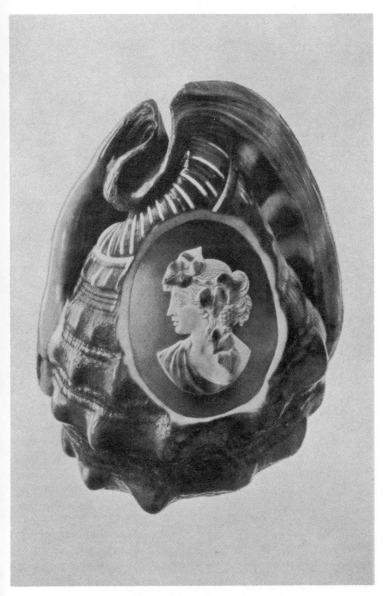

Cameo cut in a shell of *Cassis cameo*

which springs to the mind's eye at once when the word *mollusk* is mentioned, for there is scarcely a home in the land—or at least there was not in the days of my youth—that did not have an ornamental mollusk shell somewhere about. This was usually a pearly turbo, a trochid, an abalone, a cameo cut from a *Cassis cameo*, or an iridescent card tray made from a single valve of the pearl oyster. The fact that such bric-a-brac has gone out of fashion has not banished the mollusk shell completely from our homes, however, for we still find it functioning in the form of knife handles, umbrella grips, and, more intimately, pearl buttons.

It is the shell also that furnishes us with information about the antiquity of Mollusca; for their fossil shells bear evidence that these animals lived as long ago as the early part of the Paleozoic era—well-nigh the most ancient time from which animal remains of any kind are known; and the shells also bear evidence that these earliest known animals were already so highly specialized as to force us to the conclusion that their ancestors arose far back beyond Paleozoic times.

Perhaps no group of fossils is more used by the geologist and paleontologist to determine the age of geological formations than the shells of mollusks. These shells act as guides in the search for the treasures of the earth's crust, be these water, oil, iron, gold, diamonds or the thousand and one other materials that we extract from the earth.

What, then, is this thing we call a shell? It is the mollusk's skeleton, secreted by the mantle for the animal's protection. An examination of its structure—and this is true whether the shell pertains to an oyster, toothshell, snail, chiton, or even a pearly nautilus—proves it to consist of three layers: an outer thin, skinlike protective layer, called the periostracum; a thicker layer, called the prismatic, composed of elements in the form of little prisms; and an inner, very smooth, shiny layer, called the nacreous, which may or may not be pearly. The periostracum and the prismatic layer are secreted by the edge of the mantle, whereas the nacreous layer is largely secreted by the whole outside of the mantle covering.

This protective casing or exoskeleton (the shell) is of great importance in the classification of mollusks. For classificatory purposes it is comparable in value to the skeleton of the vertebrates. No other single part of the animal's anatomy tells us an equally enlightening story. The shell begins to develop at a very early stage in the mollusk's existence, frequently while the young animal is still in the egg, and certainly while it is still in the brood pouch of the parent. And unlike almost all other typical anatomic characters, this early shell is, as a rule, never shed; nor is it usually modified or overlaid with other structures. But it is added to as the animal develops, and each addition represents a stage in the life history of the species to which the particular mollusk belongs. In the shell, therefore, and permanently engraved upon it, we find a record of all the stages through which the animal has passed from birth to death. I know of no other group of organisms in the whole animal kingdom where a state of affairs so wonderfully helpful to the student obtains. As in recent, so in fossil mollusks—whether of the Pleistocene epoch, which geologically speaking was but yesterday, or of the Paleozoic era, which ran its course endless millions of years ago—the shell records the life history of the species. It is the shell then that gives us the most significant clues to the phylogeny, or racial history, of mollusks and so to their relationships.

Mollusks are found living in the tiptops of some of the tallest tropical trees and at ground level on the earth's land surface or even in the soil, in fresh water, and in the deeps of the sea. This variety of habitat is equalled by the variety of habit of these animals: there are parasitic forms; forms that live as commensals with other animals, that is, forms that live by the efforts of others though not feeding on the body substances of their hosts; forms that in some stage of their existence, at least, become permanently fixed to a support; forms that roam the high seas; and forms that crawl on the sea bottom or on land.

The adjustment of mollusks to these divers habitats and habits has of necessity entailed many modifications of form away from a generalized type; and the anatomic differences between certain members of the group and similarities between others cause us to recognize four major subdivisions or classes of the Mollusca at the present time. These are:

CLASS	EXAMPLE
Pelecypoda (hatchetfooted)	Oyster
Scaphopoda (plowfooted)	*Dentalium*
Gastropoda (bellyfooted)	Snail
Cephalopoda (headfooted)	Octopus

Of these four classes two are limited to a marine habitat; they are the Scaphopoda and the Cephalopoda. The Pelecypoda—oysters and other bivalves—occur in both fresh and salt water. Only the Gastropoda are found on the land as well as in the sea and in fresh water. In addition to being the most widely distributed, the Gastropoda, which include the snails, are by far the most numerous in species.

As to the number of species of Mollusca, I believe that if we knew all the fossil and recent forms they would total as many as a hundred and fifty thousand. This means that they are one of the largest as they are one of the most diversified of animal groups.

How long do mollusks live? That is a question that can not be answered for all forms. Where known, their duration of life extends from one to thirty years. The oyster is adult at about five years and lives for as long as ten. The garden snail has been known to live five years. The freshwater mussels, *Anodonta*, may live for thirty years.

CHAPTER II

THE BIVALVES

In the bivalves we meet, structurally speaking, the humblest of the mollusks. The clams, oysters, mussels, and their numerous kin have neither head nor jaws nor teeth. Their class name, Pelecypoda, refers to the more or less hatchet-shaped foot common to most, but not all, members of the group. What all the members do have in common is a bivalve shell—the fortress and the skeleton of its possessor—and the animals that live in bivalve shells are built more or less upon a common plan. This applies equally to the tiny *Pisidium*—which may be no larger than a pinhead and which is so prolific that its progeny fairly line the beaches of some of our lakes—and to the huge *Tridacna* (Plate 2) of the western Pacific, whose shell is sometimes used as a baptismal font.

In each valve of a pelecypod's shell may be found either one or two scars marking the places of attachment of the adductor muscles, which close the shell. Muscles which protrude or retract the foot form minor scars. Paralleling the margin is a line of close scars which show where the mantle was attached.

The general structure of the clam or oyster shell is familiar to every one. The two halves are interlocked or hinged together at the dorsal margin by various modifications of teeth, so that they can open and close at the opposite or ventral margin as do the covers of a book. Nature has displayed her customary ingenuity in these interlocking devices and has developed varied forms for the different groups of pelecypods; each form is, however, constant for each group and so serves as a valuable character for determining relationships. The adductor muscles are those that pull the two valves of the shell together, closing the mollusk in its fortress. (Incidentally, it is the single large adductor muscle of the genus *Pecten* that we eat under the name of scallop.) To open the shell when the adductor muscles are relaxed, the bivalve mollusks

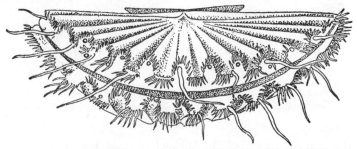

FIG. I. Scallop (*Pecten jacobaeus*). The edge of the fringed mantle bears many eyes. After Lang

depend on a ligament, which is attached to the two valves at their dorsal margins. This ligament is made up of two layers of fibrous tissue, the outer of which is nonelastic and the inner elastic. It is the inner elastic layer, or resilium, which counteracts the adductor muscles and causes the shell to gape along the ventral margins of the valves when the adductors are relaxed. In some bivalves the elastic material is distributed between the teeth of the valves and thus acts like a piece of rubber—becoming compressed when the muscles close the valves and expanding to force the valves apart when the muscles relax.

We have defined mollusks as animals enveloped in a mantle. The mantle secretes the shell, when there is one, but it has many other important and often quite unexpected functions. The edge of it can generally be seen when the shell is agape, appearing in some groups as a simple flap. In others, however, the edge bears a fringe of long and usually brilliantly colored tentacles, and in the scallops it is dotted with numerous eyes—as many as one hundred and twenty in a single animal (Fig. 1). Because we are accustomed to looking for eyes in a head, there seems something incongruous in having these organs scattered along the edge of a body covering. But

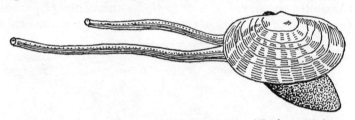

Fig. 2. Paired siphons of *Psammobia florida*. The lower siphon brings water to the gills, the upper one carries it away. After Garner

the pelecypod has no head, and as the edge of its mantle is the part of the body that looks out on the world, it is the logical place for organs of sight. Each of these mantle eyes has a cornea (or lens), a retina, and an optic nerve, so that in some respects it is singularly like the eye of vertebrates. Incidentally, the scallops do not, as a rule, live attached to one spot but are able to swim about by opening and closing the valves of their shells. This habit may help to supply a reason for the development of eyes in these forms.

But to return to the characteristics of the mantle. We find the edge usually modified at the posterior extremity into some form of paired siphons (Fig. 2), whose function is to aid the mollusks in respiration. The lower incurrent siphon brings the water to the gill chamber; the upper excurrent siphon carries it away from the animal after it has passed through the gills. These siphons differ much in size and other particulars in different groups. In some species they are scarcely indicated; in others they are prolonged to many times the length of the rest of the animal, and then they are altogether too long to be tucked away within the shell when the animal closes that organ. Such extended siphons, however, are exceptional, and in most Pelecypoda the siphons can be safely stowed away within the shell when the animal wishes to seek seclusion within its walls.

The oyster and his kin breathe by means of gills as do fishes, but mollusks use these organs for several other purposes besides respiration. In the bivalves the gills can be seen inside the mantle, looking like four combs suspended from the body. Each of the two gills has two of these combs, called lamellae or hemibranchs, and the teeth of the combs are the gill filaments. Usually the teeth are fused.

As to the several functions of molluscan gills, the one of prime importance, of course, is respiration. It is through the gills that most of the carbohydrate and fat decomposition products are eliminated from the body, and through them likewise that oxygen is taken up from the water and carried by the blood stream to the various parts of the body. To obtain oxygen the gills must have a constantly fresh stream of water; this is insured by the action of myriads of columnar cells provided with slender, hairlike lashes, called cilia, which flash more or less rhythmically and thus create a current.

A second function of the gills has nothing to do with respiration; it is food getting. The gills are covered with a layer of mucus of their own secretion. When water comes in contact with the cilia, these beat down into the mucus the microscopic life with which the water is laden, while the water is strained through the numerous pores of the gills. Once caught in the mucus, the minute prey is carried along the gill surface by the concerted action of special cilia to the labial palps. "Labial palps" means "lip appendages," and "prolonged lips" might be a very good name for those of the mollusk, for their ciliated covering seizes on the food particles and carries them to the mouth.

[9]

As we may well suppose, these various reactions of cilia and palps are automatic—just as the action of man's heart is beyond his control—and will take place so long as water flows over the mollusk's gills. Evidently, therefore, some means must be provided to prevent the mollusk choking with overmuch food and to permit it to discard undesirable catches. This last the mollusk can do at the ventral margins of its gills or through its body cavity.

Many pelecypods put their gills to a third use—that of a brood pouch. Observers of mammals can not but be surprised at such a function until they see what an efficient adaptation it is to the conditions of molluscan existence. The gills are perforated by what are called water tubes, through which flows a constant stream of water; and in these tubes many pelecypod mollusks store their fertilized eggs for further development. The brood pouch thus created is a wonderful device, for it insures the eggs both an ever-changing supply of aerated water and protection, just as do the hatching jars in our fish hatcheries. When the young have reached a definite stage of development, they are passed from the water tubes through the excurrent siphon into the great world beyond to take their chance in the battle of life.

The bivalve's gills are useful organs. And they are hard workers. By a set of very ingenious devices Dr. Paul Galtsoff, of the United States Bureau of Fisheries, has determined that an oyster works its gills for about eighteen hours a day, and that it strains water at a rate of about one gallon an hour, that is, eighteen gallons a day. Some naturalists have stated that in certain reaches of our shore line the waters sometimes contain from 1,000,000 to 2,000,000 organisms to a quart of water; using the conservative estimate of 1,000,000 to a quart or 4,000,000 to a gallon, and multiplying this by 18, we get 72,000,000 organisms that one oyster may take in a day. Multiplying this daily ration by 365 yields 26,280,000,000 organisms as the possible number an oyster may consume

PLATE 2

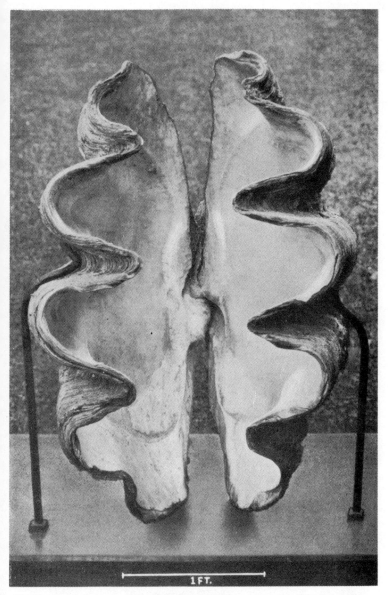

Shell of the largest of the bivalves (*Tridacna gigas*). This specimen
weighs 302 pounds

PLATE 3

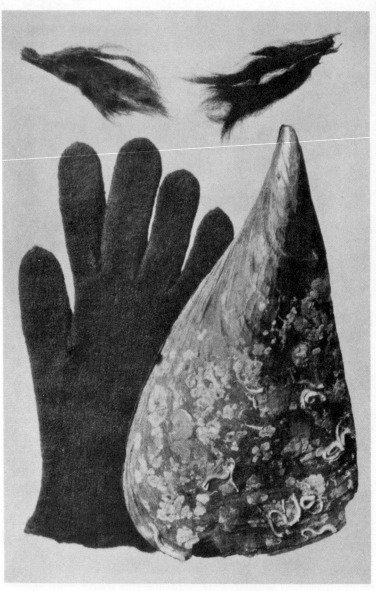

Pinna and glove woven from its byssus

in a year. To carry this a step further, we might remember that in the heyday of the oyster industry, Chesapeake Bay yielded 17,000,000 bushels a year. Since an oyster of goodly size occupies about 8 cubic inches (making 268 individuals to the bushel) the catch for one year alone might have consumed 268 times 26,280,000,000 or 7,043,040,000,000 organisms during its last year of existence. All of which shows the importance of the minute life of the sea.

Since Pelecypoda means "hatchetfooted," we have a right to expect every bearer of that name to possess a foot. Every species of Pelecypoda does have a foot at some time in its existence, and most species retain the foot through life, but some sedentary mollusks, such as the oyster, have no use for such an organ and so have none in adult life. The bivalve foot is laterally compressed, and as it is usually sharp and points downward and outward, the comparison with a hatchet is inevitable. However, it may on occasion be decidedly tongue shaped and much elongated. Naturally the form is modified from the norm to fit the foot for various specific uses, such as to aid its owner in creeping, or burrowing in mud, or digging in sand, or even drilling such hard materials as granite.

The powers of the foot are considerably augmented in certain pelecypods by the presence of a gland, which secretes the byssus. This is a bundle of tough threads of varying length and thickness, which usually resembles a tuft of hair. Certain bivalves, notably any of the black mussels, genus *Mytilus* (Fig. 3) attach themselves to some solid submerged object by means of these threads. Many species that have the capacity thus to anchor themselves seem able to break the attachment and reestablish it at will. But they can hold on with extraordinary tenacity if they choose to do so, as one may assure oneself by attempting to detach a mollusk so secured. Some species make use of the byssus as a climbing mechanism, ascending even the smooth glass side of an aquarium by its aid.

The Mediterranean peoples sometimes gather the byssus threads from the *Pinna* (Plate 3) and knit them into mittens. The fabric thus produced has a silky luster and a golden olive color.

The digestive system of an oyster and his kin, since it fulfills the same function as that of a vertebrate animal

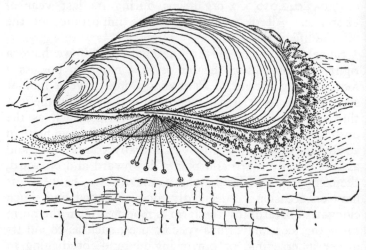

Fig. 3. *Mytilus edulis* attached by its byssus to a piece of wood.
After Möbius

and in a comparable way, may be described in the same terms. Thus the food which the labial palps transfer to the mouth passes through an esophagus to an expanded pouch, or stomach. But there is nothing faintly resembling jaws or any other masticatory apparatus. After the food has been acted on by the digestive juices in the stomach, the residue passes into an intestine, from which it is discharged from the animal's body through the excurrent siphon. Recent studies by Younge have shown that the organ in pelecypods we have been calling liver is in reality a diverticulum, or pocket, of the digestive tract, into whose pouches fine food material is carried by cilia and there digested. The white corpuscles of the blood are also credited by the same author with aiding digestion by leaving the blood vessels, ingesting food particles on the surface of the gill or intestine, and returning to the vessels.

To speak of the blood of an oyster may occasion surprise to those who are accustomed to think of this vital fluid as a red substance. The blood of bivalves is colorless, but they have a well-developed system for its circulation. The pumping mechanism—the heart—has two auricles (or chambers) for the reception of the blood from the veins after it has been charged with oxygen at the gills, and one ventricle (or chamber), for the discharge of the blood into the arteries. The arteries carry the aerated blood to all parts of the body. Once the blood has given up its oxygen to the body cells and become charged with carbon dioxide, it is collected from a system of uninclosed passages, called lacunae, into a venous sinus, whence it passes through the kidneys. Thence branchial veins carry it to the gills for aeration and others return it to the heart. Some of the blood, however, passes directly out of the venous sinus into the branchial artery, and part also passes directly into the pericardium. This causes the mixing of some of the venous blood with the arterial blood coming from the gills to the heart.

The pelecypod has no brain; its nervous system consists of three pairs of ganglia (nerve centers), each usually occupying widely separated parts of the anatomy. These ganglia furnish the nerves to the various organs of the bivalve.

In so sedentary an animal as an oyster or a mussel we should not expect to find highly developed sense organs. There are two patches of specialized cells in the mantle from which nerves lead to the visceral ganglia, and these cells are called the olfactory organs. This does not mean that bivalves have a sense of smell comparable to that of mammals: probably the function of these organs is to test the purity of the water entering by the respiratory current.

In the tentacles, siphons, mantle edge, and foot there are other sensory cells responsive to touch and possibly to other stimuli. Of greater popular interest are the auditory organs of bivalves, called otocysts. These are not ears, and their function is probably directive; that is they enable the mollusk to determine the direction of the force of gravity. They are located in the foot and consist of small pouches lined with a specialized sensory ciliated membrane; in each pouch there floats a small grain of calcareous matter. It is supposed that as the mollusk moves the tendency of this small grain of matter to fall on the particular sensory cilia which the animal's movement happens to bring into line with the force of gravity enables him to maintain his equilibrium.

To consider now the important matter of reproduction, we find that bivalves may be either of distinct sex or that one individual may have both male and female organs; that is, the individuals of some bivalve species are unisexual while those of others are hermaphroditic. Unisexuality or bisexuality does not characterize definite groups, since both phases may be present in the same genus. Usually in hermaphroditic species only one sex is ripe at a time.

Mating as observed in many animals does not occur in the pelecypods. The eggs are extruded from the ovaries and either stored away in the brood pouch of the female, as, for example, in the European oyster, *Ostrea edulis*, or cast into the water, as in the American oyster, *Ostrea virginica*. The spermatozoa are similarly ejected from the testes at the proper time. They are attracted to the ova, which they reach by swimming, whereupon fertilization takes place.

When we come to consider the fecundity of some of these bivalve mollusks, we reach figures that are staggering in their magnitude. According to Professor W. K. Brooks, the oyster is well equipped to insure the preservation of its race. He says that an unusually large American oyster will yield eggs enough to fill nearly a cubic inch of space, numbering 60,000,000 on a conservative estimate. A Maryland oyster of good size lays about 16,000,000 eggs to the brood, and if even half of these were to develop into female organisms, we should have, from a single female ancestor 8,000,000 female descendants in the first generation, and 8,000,000 times 8,000,000 or 64,000,000,-000,000 in the second generation.

Now, to continue our calculations, if each adult oyster fills 8 cubic inches of space, 8,000,000,000,000,000,000,000,000,-000,000,000,000 oysters would make a mass as large as the earth; so that the fifth generation of descendants from a single female oyster would require more space than eight planets the size of the earth, and this, even if each female laid only one brood of eggs. As the oyster lives for many years, and lays eggs each year, the possible rate of increase is very much greater than that indicated by the above figures.

More recently Dr. Paul Galtsoff, of the United States Bureau of Fisheries, has shown that a single oyster 5 inches long and 4 inches wide produced some 500,000,000 eggs in a season. If half of these produced females and there was no mortality, in the third generation this family would about equal in combined bulk half that of the earth, and in the fourth, 1,200,703 times the bulk of the earth.

The extreme fertility of the oyster means that it must have a high death rate, since otherwise the oyster would soon crowd everything else out of the sea. As it is, man's ingenuity in making use of all natural resources post-haste is rapidly depleting the once seemingly inexhaustible oyster beds. This depletion has already reached such an alarming extent that laws and regulations are being framed in every State along our seaboard to put off the evil day of the oyster's extinction. In Chesapeake Bay alone the annual output has shrunk from 17,000,000 bushels in

1875 to 2,000,000 bushels, the estimated output for 1931. A glimpse at the shell heap (Plate 4) accumulated from a year's output of one oyster-canning plant alone may help the inexperienced observer to realize the immensity of this yield. And man is not the only enemy of the oyster, for while it is in the egg or subsequent larval state it is preyed upon by almost every animal in the sea.

One of the severest restrictions on the work of the zoologist results from the fact that nature has had time and taste for so many experiments. This fact prevents me, for instance, at this moment from writing a simple history of pelecypods from the egg to the adult. Such a history would be fiction and not fact; for there are almost as many histories of Pelecypoda, as there are species in the class, and every history is different in some way from every other. In natural science generalizations are becoming more and more odious.

This much, however, is approximately true of all bivalves: Like all living things, they begin as a single cell; this cell or egg when fertilized (or sometimes even when unfertilized) passes through a series of developmental stages. Of the first three of these stages—a morula stage, a gastrula stage, and a trochosphere stage—we can make a very significant statement; namely, that they are characteristic in a general way of the forms of invertebrate life of lower rank than the mollusks, excepting protozoans and sponges. Thus the trochosphere larva of bivalves closely resembles the larva of worms at a corresponding stage of development, except for the fact that in the molluscan larva a shell gland is present which soon secretes a delicate shell. This similarity of bivalves to lower forms of life when both are in certain larval stages bears striking evidence to the truth of the theory of evolution.

Following the trochosphere the bivalves enter a larval stage which is peculiar to mollusks alone among animals. This is the free-swimming veliger stage, in which the animal acquires a membranelike swimming organ, called velum (Fig. 4). Thereafter the young mollusk gradually acquires the characteristics peculiar to the adults of the group to which it belongs.

So much for a generalized account of no bivalve in particular—an account which is roughly applicable to all bivalve young, whether they are at once cast loose on the world or harbored in the gill brood pouches of the mother through several stages of their development. When we consider specific pelecypods—the pearly fresh-water mussels found in all North American streams—we find some variant details in the larval story and an entirely new chapter added to it. The fertilized egg of this mussel finds lodging in the brood pouch of the mother and there goes through all the stages mentioned above, including the veliger. Then new changes take place, of which we shall note only two: The ventral edges of the shell may be produced into two incurved hooks armed with spines; and a glandular pouch secretes a single long thread, called the provisional byssus. In this stage the larva is called a glochidium. It remains for some little time longer in the brood pouch and is nourished by a secretion from the walls of the pouch. Eventually it is ejected with its fellow larvae through the excurrent siphon and lies on the river bottom awaiting a victim; for the glochidium, to transform into an adult mollusk, must pass a portion of its life as a parasite on the body of a suitable fish host.

We now see the reason for the incurved hooklike ventral edges of the shell, and for the provisional byssus. The glochidium lies on its back on the river bottom and extends the tiny thread up from between its shells. When this thread comes in contact with a fish, it shortens and the mussel snaps its shell into the host—either into the gills or into the skin or fins. The ferments secreted by the parasite help to bury it in the tissue of the fish, and it is nourished by the juices of its host. In this secure retreat the mussel remains for about ten weeks, undergoing the changes necessary to transform it into a miniature replica

[17]

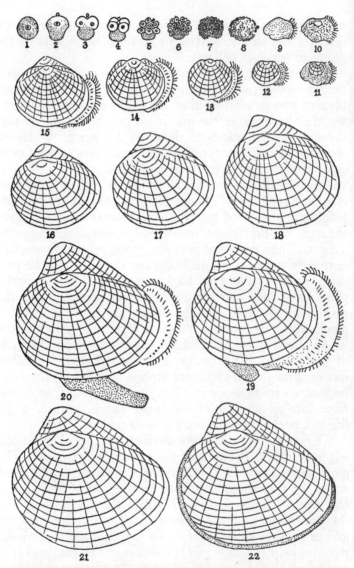

FIG. 4. Development of the East Coast oyster (*O. virginica*);
1, single cell; 6, morula stage; 8, gastrula stage; 9, trochosphere
stage; 10, veliger stage; 22, ready for attachment. After Stafford

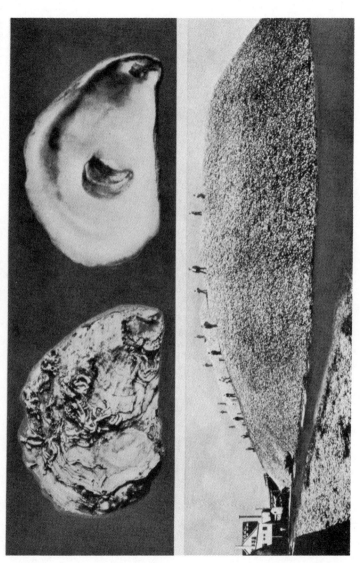

American oyster of the East Coast

Upper: Shell of *Ostrea virginica*, external and internal views. Lower: Shell heap resulting from one year's operation of a single cannery

PLATE 5

Parapholas penita burrowing in hard clay

of the adult mussel. At last fitted for an independent existence the tiny creature sallies forth to the pleasures and sorrows of adolescent and adult life.

Just any fish will not do for a host to the glochidium; most species of our pearly fresh-water mollusks demand a particular sort for their intermediate development. This fastidiousness in mussels presents problems of adjustment truly wonderful to contemplate; some species of them have become dependent upon certain migratory fishes and so spawn only when these fishes make their appearance in the stretch of water frequented by the mussels.

"Like father, like son" is true neither of the appearance nor of the habits of most bivalves. The oyster and many other pelecypods lead a sea-roving life for a time as larvae, but with the coming of adult characters they settle down to a fixed existence. Thereafter they become wholly dependent for food on what wind, wave, and current may waft to them. A larger group, including the black mussels, anchor themselves by the byssus—some permanently, others for varying periods.

There are small and seemingly fragile bivalves of the family Pholadidae which burrow into rocks as hard as granite (Plate 5). They begin by making a tiny entrance and then enlarge the chamber as they themselves grow in size, thus actually inclosing themselves in a rock-bound cell once and for all. While this may seem a confined life, it is probably a comparatively safe one, for the rock protects the frail creatures from their enemies, which would otherwise crush them. These rock-boring mollusks are sometimes sufficiently abundant to become a menace to structures built of reenforced concrete. However, when it comes to threatening human activity they are far surpassed among the mollusks by the wood borers, called shipworms (Plate 6), which are not worms at all but bivalve mollusks. The eggs of the shipworm may be cast into the sea or may be stored in the water tubes of the female to undergo part of their development. But no matter what the early stages, the larval form—after a period of free swimming—eventually seeks a piece of submerged wood in which to attain its full size. The tiny larva punctures the wood, using its shell as a drill; and once inside it grows apace, adding to its own length and to the diameter of its shell. The outer portion of the shipworm becomes fixed to the inside of the entrance of its burrow, which is guarded by a pair of minute pallets (shelly plates borne on the siphons). The pallets may be shoved into the entrance to close it when danger threatens or when the siphons, through which water is brought to the gills or carried away from them, have been withdrawn. But what tool does a bivalve mollusk have that enables it to honeycomb even hard woods with tunnels? As the animal grows the body lengthens to extraordinary proportions; and the two valves of the shell become practically a pair of hemispherical rasps or files, to which tiny teeth are added row by row. By rotation these rows of teeth are made to file away the wood. The elongate body behind the shell is, of course, shell-less and wormlike. The tiny wood filings ground off by the shell are passed into the mantle cavity and thence—with the mass of minute organisms captured by the cilia of the gills—are forwarded to the palps, and by them transferred to the mouth. Recent experiments have conclusively shown that the shipworm can use certain constituents of the wood as food—its hemicellulose content, at least. These bits are ingested in the cells of the digestive diverticula surrounding the stomach.

The shipworm continues his boring until he reaches his full size, which varies, according to the species, from six inches to four feet six inches in length and from about a sixteenth of an inch to a full inch in diameter. Then he coats his burrow with a porcellaneous lining; and once this is accomplished he becomes entirely dependent upon the food brought to him by the currents created by the cilia of his gills.

The number of young that a shipworm may produce in a season has been variously estimated at all the way from five hundred thousand to three million, depending upon the species; and since shipworms reach sexual maturity in about three months, we may readily account for the outbreaks of these pests, amounting almost to catastrophes, which have been recorded from time to time in various parts of the world. One famous outbreak occurred in San Francisco Bay in 1919 and 1920, when Beach's shipworm, *Teredo* (*Teredo*) *beachi* Bartsch, went on a rampage (Plate 7, upper), and destroyed about $21,000,000 worth of piles, wharves, and docks.

The explanation lies in the fact that two years previous to the outbreak the west coast had suffered from drought, which had so materially reduced the flow of fresh water in the Sacramento and San Joaquin rivers as to permit the invasion of salt water to Suisun Bay. With the sea water came the shipworms, and they found a forest of unprotected timbers to devour.

Losses of less extent due to shipworms are being sustained along the shores of all the seas constantly. Some species have even established themselves in fresh water. From the human point of view all shipworms are bad mollusks; that is, all are destroyers, and no wood in the sea is safe from their attack. I have seen specimens of a cargo of huge mahogany logs (Plate 7, lower) so riddled that it was impossible to cut a board a foot long and an inch thick without a burrow. The mollusks had accomplished all this devastation while the cargo was anchored near the mouth of the Ankobra River in Africa for a period of three months. Lobster pots made of lath and placed in the Bay of Maine have also been completely riddled by these pests. It is interesting to note here that when a large species of shipworm attacks a small bit of wood like a lath, it fails to develop into full size. At maturity it is still dwarfed in all its characters and thus

[21]

forms a miniature of the normal creature. I have called such stunted forms "stenomorphs."

No wood so far found seems impervious to shipworms. We are often told that this or that variety of wood possesses toxic qualities, which make it shipworm resistant, but when put to the test such woods always fail to stand up. Even the toxic greenheart wood of the American Tropics used for the sills and striking strips of the Panama Canal failed to resist the shipworms; and yet this wood is so poisonous that a man who was immune to berberine—its toxin—had to be brought to the Canal Zone from England to shape the timbers. The very largest of the American shipworms, *Bankia (Nausitora) dryas* Dall, (Plate 6, Nos. 9, 12, 13, 17) was found infesting the roots of living mangroves in Peru, although mangrove timber had been reputed immune. Floating coconuts also became honeycombed, in spite of the fact that palm wood is said to be free from attack.

I know of but one shipworm whose existence seems to leave a balance on the credit side of man's ledger, and that one lives in far-off Siam, where—so Dr. Hugh M. Smith tells us—it is purposely cultivated in soft wood planted at the mouth of streams. After three months the wood is taken up and split, and the shipworms that have by this time riddled it are collected and sold for food. They are relatives of the oyster, and my limited experience permits me to proclaim them the oyster's equal, if not superior, so far as flavor is concerned.

Other groups of bivalves, also, have a predilection for destroying wood—the *Xylophaga*, for example; but none are so completely destructive as those we have just discussed—the members of the family Teredinidae—which rapidly convert into pulp any piece of wood that may be carried to the sea, unless it is protected from their attacks by man.

Still another group of bivalves become what are known as nestlers, because they tuck themselves away into con-

PLATE 6

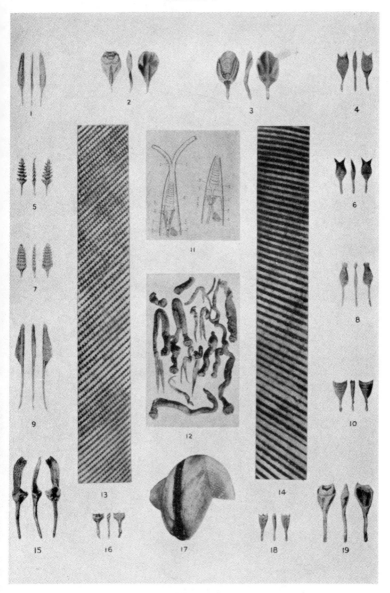

Shipworms

1-10, 15, 16, 18, 19, shelly pallets borne on the siphons of various shipworms, which serve as doors to their tunnels; 11, mechanism for closing door; 12, animals of *Bankia setacea*; 13, 14, cutting files of *Nausitoria dryas* much enlarged; 17, shell of same

PLATE 7

Damage by shipworms
Upper: Wharf in San Francisco Bay, which collapsed in 1920 as a
result of boring in piles by shipworms. Lower: Piece of mahogany log,
completely riddled

venient nooks and sometimes enlarge these to suit their
needs. The giant *Tridacna*, whose shell (see Plate 2)
is sometimes used as a baptismal font, stretches himself
on his back in some coral-reef cranny and permits the reef
to grow about him. We are told by Doctor Mayer
that coral reefs grow at the rate of two inches a year
in the western Pacific. I have several times seen this
monster bivalve clamped in a reef, though he was always
able to open his shell sufficiently to show the glorious
edge of the peacock-colored mantle within.

By far the greater number of pelecypods exhibit a more
orthodox behavior in making themselves comfortable and
use the foot (Fig. 5) to anchor themselves in the ooze on

Fig. 5.   Cockle (*Cardium edule*) with digging
foot extended at left; anal and branchial siphons
at right. Modified from Möbius

the floor of stream, lake, or ocean, or to transport themselves slowly from place to place as need or inclination
prompts them. In reaches of bottom where sandy mud
predominates, you may find the razor clam nicely buried,
another exploit which must be credited to the wonderful digging foot (Fig. 6). And on the mud flats, the
"mercenary Venus," our hard-shelled clam, or quahog,
and the soft-shelled clam must be dug from the hiding
places which they themselves have excavated. These
and other mollusks, as, for example, *Psammobia florida*

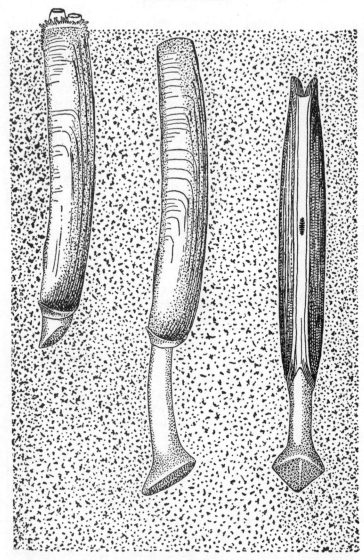

FIG. 6. Razor clams (*Ensis directus*) illustrating use of the digging foot. Left, preparing to extend foot; center, foot extended and expanded; right, anchored foot drawing the animal down. Modified from Drew

PLATE 8

Pearls from fresh-water mussels of the Mississippi River.   Courtesy of Nature Magazine

PLATE 9

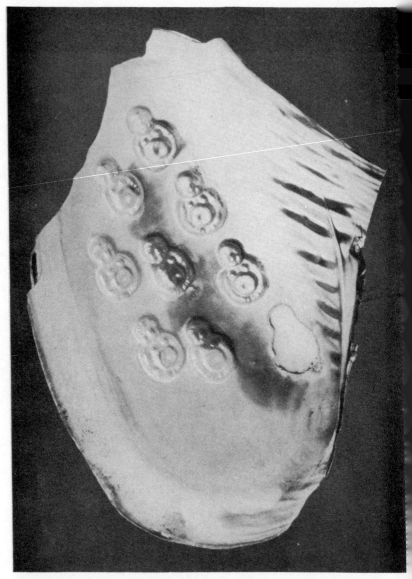

Shell of Chinese fresh-water mussel with tin images of Buddha coated with nacre

THE BIVALVES

(see Fig. 2, page 8), dig way down deep to find a snug retreat, and they communicate with the outer world by means of two long siphons.

Not all bivalves are sluggish or slow-moving creatures. If you doubt this statement, try the following experiment along any part of our Middle or South Atlantic coast: Dip up a netful of sand from an incoming wave (using a fine-meshed dip net), and when the sand has sifted out of the net examine what is left behind. You will find a collection of *Donax*. Place them in a dish of water with a supply of sand in the bottom, and instantly the bivalves will right themselves and slip beneath the sand—an excellent object lesson in mollusk speed.

Still more interesting than the *Donax* are the scallops, which dart away by rapidly opening and closing their shells when danger threatens. They are wonderful creatures, provided sometimes, as has been stated, with as many as 120 eyes around the mantle edge. These eyes warn their owners of approaching danger.

It would not be just to the bivalves to leave them without calling attention to the usefulness to man of the group as a whole, for we have already condemned some of its members as harmful—the shipworms. But the useful members make up by far the majority of the group, and of them we will now speak.

The bivalve which ranks highest in dollar value is the oyster. Statistics show that among all the animals of the sea only the herring exceeds the oyster in the annual financial profit which the marine fisheries reap from its sale.

The shells of many bivalves, also, are useful to man. They were once much sought after as ornaments—the pearly ones, especially; and they have often served as money, particularly among primitive peoples. For this latter purpose sometimes small bits instead of the whole shell are preferred. The American Indians from Maine to Texas used to make wampum by cutting and grinding beads from the shell of our hard clam, *Venus mercenaria*, and drilling and stringing them. By selecting the white or blue areas of the shell the Indians were able to make white or blue beads, which, at the time of the white man's arrival, constituted the favored coin of the country. In the Philippines and other parts of the Orient, *Placuna placenta*—the window shell—is much used in windows in place of glass. These shell windows tone down the glare of the tropical sun and are much more restful for the eyes and more serviceable than an equal expanse of glass would be.

No account of bivalves would be complete without a mention of pearls. In Volume 3 of the Smithsonian Scientific Series (pp. 217-224) will be found a fuller discussion of pearls than we have space for in this paper, but we can not pass them by here without at least a word.

Pearls, as everybody knows, are found in mollusk shells. They are the result of an effort on the part of the mollusk to seal up an enemy or an irritating substance that has found its way inside the shell or has bored into the animal's flesh. The most perfect spherical pearls usually have as their initial incentive the baby stage of a fluke worm that must live for part of its early life in a mollusk. These young worms burrow into the flesh of the host and live upon it until they have attained a certain growth. The host, to overcome this undesirable parasite, attempts to lock it up by secreting a shelly capsule around it; and if successful it kills the parasite in that way. But having once begun to secrete nacre—the shiny substance of the pearly shell—the mollusk can't stop, and so it builds layer upon layer around the nucleus.

The irregularly shaped pearls known as "baroques" usually begin when a grain of sand or some other hard foreign substance is accidentally forced into the mantle cavity of the mollusk, whereupon the bivalve promptly walls off the intruded matter against the inside of the shell and adds to the wall, layer after layer, the smooth

PLATE 10

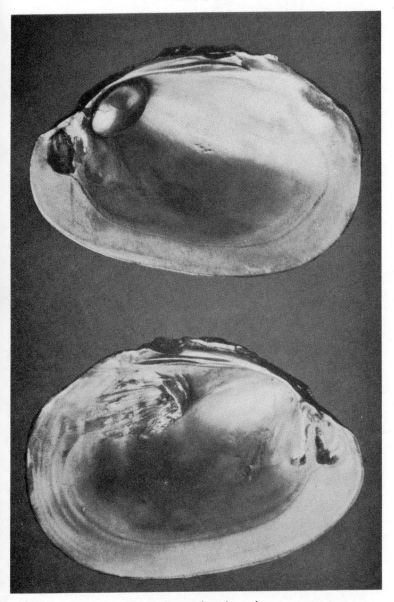

American cultural pearls
Upper: A perfectly shaped specimen, which cracked as a result of being removed while still immature. Lower: A mishap which resulted when the wax spread upon insertion under the mantle

coating reducing the irritation. Sometimes little water mites related to our chigres attack in large numbers the gills of our fresh-water clams, often causing the irregular "rose" pearls to form. Again, a small fish or crustacean may dart into the mantle cavity seeking protection from some pursuer. This intruder, too, will be walled off, fixed to the inside of the mollusk shell, and covered with nacre until the excrescence so formed develops into a pearl having the shape of the fish or shrimp.

The National Museum possesses some specimens of shells of a huge fresh-water pearl mussel from the Far East, on the inside of which are numerous little images of Buddha, all done in pearl (Plate 9). We are told that these are sold to or bestowed upon pilgrims visiting certain sacred shrines and that they are highly valued by the Orientals as miraculous manifestations of Buddha. These little images are really the forerunners of our "cultural pearls"—the trade name for our artificially grown gems. To produce the pearl images the Buddhist priest inserted a small wooden wedge between the two valves of the mussel, when these were open, to keep them from closing. This made it possible for him to work in the interior. Next he carefully forced the mantle for a little way from its attachment to the inner bottom edge of the shell, and inserted between the mantle and the shell a number of small images of Buddha, stamped in tin, upon the underside of which he placed some sticky substance—probably a bit of beeswax. He then restored the mussel to the pool from whence he had taken it and where he knew it would shortly repair the injury done to the edge of the mantle and would also overcome the irritation produced by the irregular surface of the tin images by coating them with nacre. When he took these mussels from the pool a few months later the images had become fixed to the inside of the shells in just the position in which they had been placed; but now they were nicely

coated with shining pearly nacre—miraculous manifestations of the Great Buddha.

The introduction of foreign elements of various kinds
into the shells of live bivalves has been practiced for a long
time by many peoples; but the pearls thus produced have
usually been inferior, because metals used as a nucleus in
such work are apt to cause the nacre to become stained
and therefore imperfect.

CHAPTER III

THE TOOTHSHELLS

THE bivalves are headless and toothless, but, as we have seen, quite competent to live their own lives for all that. All the other classes of mollusks, however, have both head and teeth. In some groups the head is well developed and in others extremely rudimentary. As to teeth all the mollusks except the bivalves and a few gastropods are similarly equipped; that is, all of them have in the mouth a ribbonlike organ, called the radula, which is furnished with numerous teeth.

Of a low type of organization, the Scaphopoda constitute a class, not so widely known and alike of less value and of less danger to human economy than any other class of mollusks. But the naturalist who accepts ecoomic value as his criterion of interest will soon find himself doubly betrayed—robbed of the essential equipment for his calling, which is a catholic curiosity avid of every secret in nature, and cheated of finding the very pots of gold for which he seeks; for in the history of science it has repeatedly happened that the most useful secrets, such for instance as the X-ray, have come to light accidentally in the search for truth.

We need not therefore brush the Scaphopoda aside merely because they occupy but little space in the scheme of human economy. Unfortunately little work has actually been done on the soft parts of these animals or on their habits, and there are innumerable facts about their structure and ways of life of which we are totally ignorant. One of the reasons why the scaphopods are so little known to the public, no doubt, is that they are found only in the sea, and most of them only in the deeps thereof. They range in practically all seas from a little below the low-tide mark to depths of several hundred fathoms. Furthermore, they are little given to traveling but prefer apparently to remain forever in the spot where they begin adult life. The foot with which every scaphopod is provided is used to move the animal, but only directly or obliquely downward. The foot is a burrowing organ, and Scaphopoda means "plowfooted." In burrowing the foot is thrust into the sand; its free end is then expanded to give the mollusk anchorage; and finally muscular contraction pulls the shell headforemost into the hole after the foot. The scaphopod does not bury the entire shell but leaves the hind end of it sticking up into the sea. As the head is thus in permanent darkness, eyes would be useless; so we are not surprised to find that the animal has none.

Toothshell—a name commonly applied to the Scaphopoda—describes the shell or skeleton peculiar to this class of mollusks very well, for it is always notched at the front end. The shell is of a type found in no other mollusk (Plate 11). Secreted by the tubular mantle, it is closed around the animal, but both ends are open. The typical form is long and tapering; but in one genus, *Cadulus*, the shell does not taper regularly but swells out at some point or other in the length, so that some species are cask-shaped and others look like a snake that has swallowed an egg.

Scaphopod shells exhibit but few colors, and there are no gay patterns. Plain white, green, and brown to reddish are all the colors their palette affords. The whites may be chalky or translucent. Not many styles of sculpture are found. The greater number of these shells are smooth, but they may have a few or numerous riblets running along their entire length. The range in size is very great. The largest shell that has come to my notice

PLATE 11

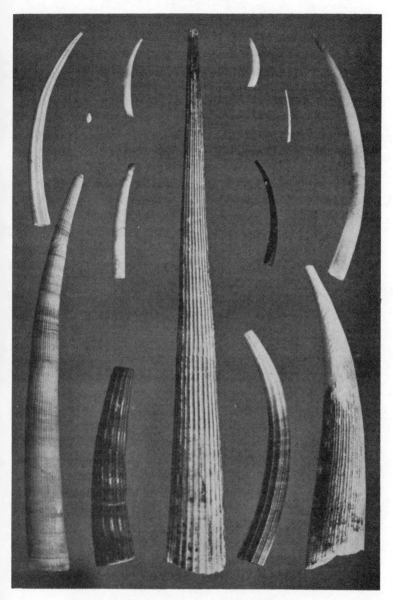

Representative scaphopod shells

we dredged during the cruise of the steamer *Albatross* (of the United States Bureau of Fisheries) off the Philippine Islands, at a depth of 281 fathoms. This has a length of about six and five-sixteenths inches, and a diameter of about eleven-sixteenths of an inch. Some, especially in the genus *Cadulus*, are quite minute. For instance, one species has a length of but a tenth of an inch.

In the embryonic stage of the-Scaphopoda the shell is flasklike and the upper or posterior end is closed. Shortly after hatching it becomes toothlike, loses the baby shell, and is then open at both ends. Both the anterior and posterior orifices are minute at the beginning but necessarily become larger as the animal grows. As the shell enlarges in diameter at the anterior end, the animal absorbs a portion of the apex so as to make the orifice there larger. The larger end is the front end, and from its generally circular orifice the cylindrical head and long foot are protruded. The function of the orifice at the upper end of the shell is to allow the discharge of the genital products and the wastes of digestion and respiration.

The head of Scaphopoda, if it may be called such, is an egg-shaped projection, which extends into the mantle cavity and at the apex of which is the mouth. This head is surrounded by a rosette of lobes, possibly organs of touch. Farther back are a pair of lobes each bearing many tentacles, which are probably respiratory in function. A number of threadlike "captacula" (Fig. 7) spring from the base of the snout. So called because they catch the Foraminifera and minute bivalve mollusks which form part of the food of the scaphopods, the captacula—true to their name—are thrust in the sand in all directions in search of food, and convey it to the funnel-shaped mouth. Then the masticatory apparatus comes into play. This consists of a tongue or radula, armed with five rows of sharp spines, one in the middle and two on each side. A rotary motion of the tongue enables the spines to rasp off portions of food, which are then passed to the stomach.

The possession of a rudimentary head by this class of mollusks does not involve the possession of a brain. The nervous system of a scaphopod, like that of a bivalve, consists of three pairs of ganglia or nerve centers. Unlike

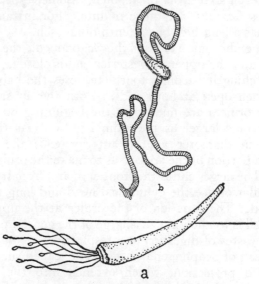

FIG. 7. *Dentalium vulgare;* a, animal in feeding position in the sand with captacula extended; b, one of the captacula greatly enlarged. After Lacaze-Duthiers

the bivalve, the scaphopod has no heart; and the blood does not circulate through well-defined arteries and veins but only through sinuses.

As to whether or not the members of this class possess the senses, indicated in most animals by appropriate organs, the evidence is meager. We do know, however, that the scaphopod is blind. Probably he can hear—to a slight degree, at least—for he possesses numerous otolites or ear stones. These are calcareous and globular and are inclosed in two nearly spherical pouches, lined with vibratile cilia, which are in constant action and agitate the otolites by an incessant tremulous movement. The lobes at the base of the head are probably tactile organs.

Man today has little use for the scaphopods, but in the days gone by their shells played an important role in the ornamentation of primitive man's dress. Cut in sections they served as beads among the North American Indians. They are likewise said to have been used as the standard of value in trade among the Indians of the Northwest before the Hudson Bay Company substituted blankets for that purpose. A slave was valued at a fathom—from twenty-five to forty of these shells strung lengthwise.

CHAPTER IV

THE SNAILS AND THEIR ALLIES

THE stalked eyes and the silvery trail of slime of the garden snail are familiar sights in the experience of all but the most urban of city dwellers; rather repulsive sights, too, due to an aversion to the connotations of the word *slime*. Applied to snails this is quite an illogical aversion, since the garden variety is a cleanly vegetarian with a marked preference for the tenderest of lettuce leaves. A catalogue of the likes and dislikes, taboos and preferences of all the groups of the human race would yield some interesting reading, little of it flattering to human intelligence. Most Americans abhor snails; Frenchmen eat them for the delicacy they are. Yet a Frenchman of Brittany hesitates to eat the fine fruit of the blackberry bushes that line his fields and roads, and for generations white men considered the tomato unfit for food.

But to return to our snails. Those met with in gardens represent but a few among thousands of species of the class Gastropoda, which embraces a larger number of species and of individuals than any other class in the entire sub-kingdom of mollusks. The better-known members of the class go by the popular names of snail, slug, limpet, whelk, periwinkle, sea hare and coat-of-mail shell. They occur everywhere, from the tree tops to the deeps of the sea; they include land forms, water forms, and amphibious forms; they are shelled and shell-less; they are of all sizes from less than that of a tiny pinhead up to a length of two feet, which is the size attained by the big horse conch, *Fasciolaria gigantea* (Plate 12). Finally, they supply mankind with many things, among them, food, dyes, umbrella handles, and—indirectly—diseases.

This matter of gastropod distribution involves some rather curious facts. Civilized man is a ubiquitous animal, capable of living either at the poles or at the Equator. But most other animals lack this ability; they must live in the environment for which they are specially adapted. Thus we find that each area of the earth has its own localized fauna. This is true of the sea as well as of the land, the factors that determine the distribution of species in the sea being temperature, salinity, depth, pressure, character of bottom, and chemical content of the water. Certain groups of mollusks are so delicately adjusted to certain combinations of these factors that they can live under those combinations and no other. The layman would be little apt to guess at the fruitfulness of this fact to the paleontologist. Give him a lot of fossil mollusk shells laid down in some ancient sea and he can readily reconstruct a picture of the bottom and determine such facts as the amount of movement to which the covering sea was subject, its temperature, and salinity. With equal ease the malacologist—student of present-day mollusks—can give a picture of the habitat and name the faunal area from which a collection of recent mollusks have been taken.

Some snails are restricted within almost unbelievably narrow limits. Thus most of the species of the beautiful Hawaiian tree snails, *Achatinella* (Plate C), are confined to a single island and to a single valley in that island. An aviator who happens to be a malacologist (inconceivable hypothesis), and who makes a forced landing in this valley need only pick a snail from a tree to learn his exact location.

What is perhaps the most restricted range of any animal in existence is that of the dwarf cerion (*Cerion nana*), a species of snails mentioned by Maynard as occurring on the island of Little Cayman, in the Caribbean Sea, in an area only five or six yards wide by twenty long. Maynard found snails of this species there in 1888; and I found descendants of the same colony occupying practically the same space in 1930, forty-two years later.

The genus *Achatinella*, of Hawaii, the Philippine tree snails of the genus *Cochlostyla* (see Plate D), and *Amphidromus*, and the garishly colored snails that inhabit the eastern end of Cuba, *Polymita picta* (see Plate E), offer exceptional problems to the student of genetics and heredity because of the remarkable differentiation from the typical form which has taken place in them. Each in fact occupies a territory that may be considered a glorified laboratory, in which nature, beginning in comparatively recent times, has been experimenting to produce the products seen in our pictures. Each one of these groups enables the knowing eye to discern the factors involved in its differentiation. The workshops are still present, and the tools of hybridization, isolation, and fixation are still at hand.

Although most marine snails are closely circumscribed in habitat, it is possible to find some of them living above the high-tide line of the sea, for example, at Koko Head, Oahu, Hawaiian Islands. The key to this paradox lies in the action of the breakers. They have cut away the edge of the island and produced sea cliffs of considerable height, from the top of which the land slopes back gently, with many pits and depressions in its lava surface. The long rolling waves break against the cliff, smothering the space above them with spray and spume to varying heights, depending upon the condition of the sea; though even with a quiet sea the swell breaks constantly over the rim. This spray carries with it larval creatures of many kinds and strands them in the pools and puddles, so that they establish themselves there. One can find quite a molluscan marine fauna and many other animals flourishing way above the level of the sea, each wave bringing a new supply of water and food to them.

PLATE 12

The two largest of the gastropod shells. Left, horse conch (*Fasciolaria gigantea*); right, *Fusus proboscidiferus*

PLATE 13

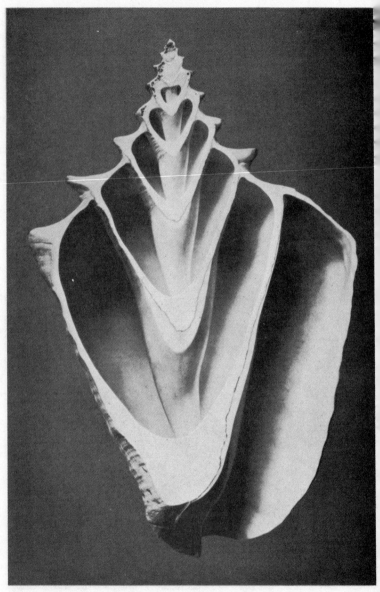

Longitudinal section of the shell of *Strombus gigas* illustrating the spiral coiling

THE SNAILS AND THEIR ALLIES

Two other groups of marine gastropods (to be discussed later), have won for themselves a larger horizon than that of most of their relations. They have become adapted to a free-swimming existence and spend their lives roaming the deeps.

STRUCTURE AND FUNCTIONS

The shells of gastropods are like human nature—infinite in their diversity. The more usual forms are in reality cones, which have been coiled to economize space. Each of them begins as a tiny capsule, to which constant additions are made at the open or mouth end until it attains its full size (Plate 13). The shells are almost always spirally coiled, usually to the right, but not always so. Right-handed species very rarely take a left-handed turn, and the left-handed forms are equally careful about their behavior. Some, however, like *Amphidromus*, are not so particular; and offspring from the same mother may include both dextral and sinistral individuals. Some species, like the limpets (Plate 14, No. 9), seem to have no whorls, but only a cuplike dome; though many limpetlike forms show the tiny coils in their baby stages.

To paraphrase Napoleon, one picture is worth ten thousand words describing the surfacing of the spiral shells of gastropods. Plate 15 shows some of the many different kinds of surfaces found in the shells of the genus *Murex* alone—polished, granular, spined, knobbed, ribbed axially or spirally and the ribs varying in magnitude from hairlike to cordlike; or the sculpture may consist of incised elements of varying strength. Why this variety? Some of the features undoubtedly add strength to the mollusk's housing and others increase its defense efficiency against the ravages of fish and other enemies. But the wherefore of many remains a mystery to man.

A group of "worm" shells from Bermuda—*Vermetus lumbricalis* (Plate 16)—betrays a curious departure from the norm of spiral shells. These mollusks begin with

[37]

orthodox, spirally coiled shells; but they break with convention at last and assume the form shown in the illustration.

Some shells plume themselves with borrowed feathers. The marine snail *Xenophora*, appropriately known as the collector, has acquired the habit of bedecking himself with the empty shells of other mollusks as well as with sand grains, bits of coral, and similar detritus from the sea bottom. The collector affixes these decorations into his shell near the suture as the shell is secreted (Plate 17). This habit probably began as a protective measure, most likely when *Xenophora* first evolved; for no matter what species we examine—even one that seems free of such bedecking—we will always find at least a trace of shell fragments on the early turns. Apparently mollusks, like men, find it difficult to overcome an acquired habit.

There is another character of the gastropod shell structure which presents fascinating features and problems. I refer to the aperture. The shape of this reveals an endless series of modifications in the different species, some of which are shown in Plate 18. The aperture, of course, is the gate of the mollusk's fortress; and the security thereof is no greater than the effectiveness of the guard at this gate. Many gastropods—terrestrial, fresh-water, marine—have a kind of door, called operculum, which closes them in the shell. Some supplement this door with other defensive devices, a number of which are shown in Plate 19. All these devices are based upon the thickening of the edge of the aperture or a part thereof, or upon its contraction, or upon the possession of lamellae.

The gastropod carries his door on his foot. This is the most logical position possible for the structure, since it is the foot that brings up the rear when the animal retreats into his shell, and so permits the door, or operculum, automatically to close the aperture when the foot has passed through it. Some authorities offer the interesting suggestion that the operculum represents the equivalent of

[38]

PLATE 14

Representative gastropod shells, showing great range of shapes

PLATE 15

Shells of *Murex*, to show different kinds of surfacing in a single genus

the second valve of the pelecypods; that is, that the gastropods have evolved from a bivalve form, one valve becoming the twisted cone and the other the operculum.

The opercula in gastropods almost equal their shells in variety of surfacing, as is indicated in Plate 20. In its least specialized form, the door is a simple plate of chondrin, a substance allied to the material of which a crab's shell is composed. This plate is present as the basal element in all opercula, although in some it is so thin that it forms a mere film.

Incidentally the operculum of some groups of gastropods revives the oft-asked question as to why some things in nature are so beautiful. The under side of the operculum in the groups to which I refer, that is, the part attached to the foot and so permanently hidden during life from the eyes of man and beast, may be wonderfully banded with rays of brown and green. Why is it so beautiful? Evidently there is no reason at all.

The closing of the door to evade enemies that may camp at the doorstep indefinitely to await its opening, has resulted—at least, so one may assume—in the development of all sorts of devices that will enable the animal to breathe while the closed door defies the would-be invader. In the American family of operculated land shells—the Annulariidae—these devices include a simple slit in the upper angle of the aperture, a simple puncture, and a perforated tube or siphon too fine to admit the undesirables.

However, not all gastropods are equipped with a door to close the shell or even a supplementary device to keep out undesirable visitors. This lack likewise presents the problem of keeping in moisture, notably to certain tropical land forms, during the parching days of a tropical dry season. Many of the species so handicapped have solved this problem by spinning, or rather, secreting, an epiphragm. The epiphragm in its simplest form is nothing more than a film of dried slime. In some snails, however, it is supplemented and strengthened by the addition of lime salts. The epiphragm hermetically seals the animal within its shell when it aestivates and prevents the loss of the moisture needed for its existence. The epiphragm is dropped when the animal resumes an active existence at the beginning of the moist season. Plate 21 shows *Cepolis ovumreguli*, from eastern Cuba, tucked away in an old palm leaf for a dry spell.

Incidentally, some gastropods are capable of even greater refinements of spinning than that just described. Like spiders they spin threads by which to suspend themselves, in mid-air, from a shelf of rock or from the roof or side of a cave. This capacity seems to play some part in the love-making of the slugs of the species *Limax maximus*. After executing a nuptial dance, a pair of these slugs will spin a thread and by it drop free from some overhanging support during mating. After the performance they will climb back to solid ground via the thread.

The ornamentation of the gastropod shell is not confined solely to sculpture, for many shells are wonderfully colored, as the color plates in this chapter show. No matter what hues may be present or how intricate the pattern they form, I have yet to see them so assembled or combined as to sound a false note. The commercial artist might well appeal to shell coloring and shell sculpture for models of beauty in tone and form. So far as I am aware, only one people—the Japanese—are awake to the rich treasures presented in this field.

It may be that the wonderful coloring of some species of gastropods helps to conceal them from their enemies. Yet in many species we know it can serve no purpose. The beautiful shell of the tentshell (*Oliva porphyria*), in the Gulf of California (see Plate A, No. 6), is completely hidden by the animal's mantle. I recall my frequent chagrin in turning over coral blocks in the shallow reaches of the Philippine seas in quest of nudibranchs—beautifully colored sluglike gastropods, usually

PLATE 16

A departure from the norm in so-called worm shells (*Vermetus lumbricalis*) from Bermuda

PLATE 17

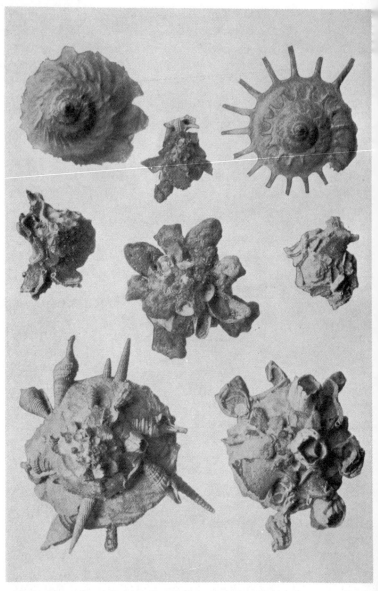

Shell of *Xenophora*, the collector, with decoration affixed during growth

shell-less in the adult stage—on seeing some gorgeous creature slowly retreat into a shell and so proclaim itself a cowrie. All the cowries, prodigal of beauty, wrap the glory of their shells in a mantle which itself might dispute with anything in nature for the crown of loveliness.

So much for the more usual type of shell in the Gastropoda—the spirally wound cone with its infinity of variants. Some gastropods, for example certain slugs, have no shell at all; or, at best, they have but a small internal shelly plate. As the adult oyster has dispensed with a useless foot, so have these slugs dispensed with a useless shell. This is a common phenomenon in nature— to discard what has become superfluous—so that we are not surprised to encounter it in some of the gastropods. However, we may find cause for wonder in the extraordinary modification of the molluscan shell exhibited by the chitons of the subclass Amphineura—the coat-of-mail shells (Plate 22). In the chitons the shell consists of eight pieces, or plates, which cross the animal like the armor of an armadillo and completely protect it. The plates are imbricated, that is, slightly overlapping, and articulated and may be smooth or variously sculptured. They grow out of a section of the mantle called the girdle, which may be a narrow band or may cover the entire upper part of the animal.

The shell of a chiton is further distinguished by the possession of eyes. According to A. H. Cooke, *Corephium aculeatum* has as many as 12,000 eyes, of which more than 3,000 are found in the head plate. The largest known chiton eyes measure a thirty-fifth of an inch in diameter. It is possible that these "eyes" have some value as visual organs, for many of them have cornea, lens, pigment layer with iris, and retina; however, their power of vision must be low.

Chitons are all dwellers in the sea, ranging from the high-tide level to the deeps. When dislodged from their anchorage they curl up like an armadillo or a pill-bug, but if undisturbed they will eventually uncurl and move off to some hiding place.

Gastropods are so called because the better known kinds appear to walk on their abdomens (Fig. 8). Scientific attempts at descriptive nomenclature have rarely

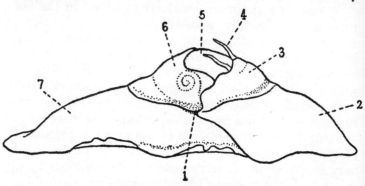

FIG. 8. *Natica josephina;* 1, exhalant orifice; 2, propodium, or forefoot; 3, part of propodium extending over shell; 4, tentacles; 5, shell; 6, part of metapodium extending over shell; 7, metapodium, or hind foot

been so successful: certainly "bellyfooted" is an apt name for a snail. Like everything else in the gastropod cosmos, however, the foot is subject to innumerable modifications in different groups, resulting, of course, from the wide range in methods of progression in the class.

Thus in the genera *Melampus* and *Pedipes*, a groove separates the fore part of the foot from the middle part. When moving the animal seems to step along: it extends and fixes the fore part then draws up the rest like a leech, moving—so to speak—in a series of loops. In many of the annulariids the sole is divided lengthwise by a groove, and such species progress by alternately moving the two sides. The resultant motion in some is, in miniature, like the swaying of an elephant, or the waddling of a very fat puppy but of course much slowed up. The broad sole of the foot in the sea-ears (*Haliotis*, Plate 23, upper left),

PLATE 18

Shells of land, fresh-water, and marine gastropods, to show differences in shape of the aperture

PLATE 19

Shells of land and marine gastropods, to show kinds of armature of the aperture

limpets, and chitons enables these mollusks to secure a firm hold on their support by suction—so firm that it is almost impossible for a man to dislodge one of the larger members of these groups. In fact, there are records of men having been captured by the mollusks, instead of the reverse. The huge sea-ears or abalones have not only a wonderfully iridescent pearly shell but also a toothsome flavor, which, before the supply became decidedly limited, caused them to appear regularly at the fish marts of the California coast towns. It seems that more than one stroller by the sea who was acquainted with sea-ears as a market delicacy has happened upon one at extreme low tide fastened to a rock, and unaware of the amazing strength with which the foot can hold on to its place of attachment, has slipped a hand under the slightly raised shell to pull it off. Instead of succeeding in this intention the luckless man had his hand caught under the clamped-down shell. The more he struggled the tighter the mollusk would hold on. The incoming tide would in time put an end to struggle and life alike, and only then would the weary *Haliotis* loose its hold. The bruised fingers of the drowned victim would tell the tale of the battle for life, in which the mollusk won.

These mollusks that cling tightly to rocks, from which, once they have clamped down, only a knife can pry them loose, may be readily dislodged from their anchorage by a sudden jar or sidelong shove, if they are caught unawares before they contract.

Some gastropods use the foot as a float; that is, they expand it in such a way that it becomes broad and flat, and exposing the sole to the air they move about at the surface in an inverted position. *Physa* and some *Lymnaea*, fresh-water mollusks that often grow in aquariums, frequently indulge in this pastime.

In many gastropods the foot has been transformed into an efficient swimming organ. Notably is this true of two subclasses, the Pteropoda and Heteropoda, the free-

[43]

swimming groups which have been referred to earlier in this chapter as rovers of the sea. Their names mean "wingfooted" and "diversefooted." The Pteropoda (Fig. 9) have the anterior lobes of the foot developed

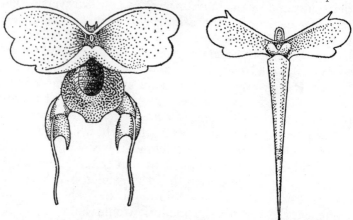

Fig. 9. Representative Pteropoda, with foot transformed into swimming wings. Left, butterfly pteropod (*Hyalaea limbata*); right, *Creseis subula*, with long shell. After De la Sagra

into two broad thin winglike organs with which they swim at or near the surface.

The modification of the heteropod foot (Fig. 10) for swimming is of a different sort; the entire foot has become a sort of median fin, and the animal swims back downward.

The Pteropoda with their wingfeet frequently match the butterfly in brilliance of coloring. Though small, these gastropods are so numerous that at times they cover the surface of the sea for miles and constitute the main article of diet for many fishes and cetaceans. The shell that incases the pteropod is thin, frequently a mere film, usually transparent as glass and often even more fragile. When one captures these creatures in a plankton net and liberates them in a bowl of sea water for study, one does not always feel sure that they are actually present in the dish. Their extremely delicate structure suggests often but a bit of jelly, and that is so transparent that it fails to obstruct the view of whatever lies beyond it.

No discussion of the gastropod foot would be complete that did not touch on one matter that must surely have excited the curiosity of everyone who has seen a slug

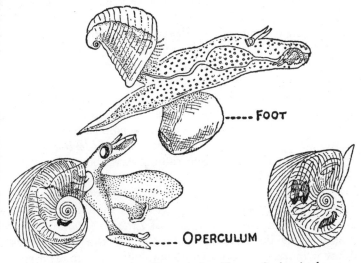

FIG. 10. Representative Heteropoda. Upper, *Carinaria;* lower left, *Atlanta;* right, same withdrawn into transparent shell. After Eydoux and Souleyet

drawing his silver trail along a garden path: How does he make the trail and why? It is made by a secretion from glands in the foot of land mollusks, and its purpose seems to be to smooth the passage of the snail. In other words the snail is his own road maker and carries with him a superior liquid surfacing. The silvery glint of the trail comes out when the secretion dries after the snail has passed. "Go slowly, go surely, and you will leave a brilliant trail," admonishes the snail.

Because a certain gastropod lives in water we need not conclude that he breathes by means of gills; nor because another lives on land that he has lungs. Among the gastropods there are lung-breathing aquatic forms and there are also gill-breathing terrestrial forms. The genera *Lymnaea*, *Physa*, and *Planorbis* spend their lives in fresh water, yet they must come to the surface periodically to fill the lung with air. They are like the whales, which are born and live in the water, yet breathe as do all other mammals.

But the exchange of an aquatic home for a terrestrial one does not necessitate the exchange of gills for lungs. The traveler in Florida or the West Indies can scarcely have failed to notice the countless numbers of snails (genus *Tectarius*) clinging to the rocks well above high-tide level. Our *Littorina irrorata* climbs up on the beach grass at the Virginia capes, while *Littorina rudis* decorates the northern rocks above high tide, and *Littorina angulifera* clings to the mangrove roots away above the water mark along our Florida Keys. All of these are gill breathers, yet they seem to shun the water, probably visiting it only often enough to keep the gills moist. Herdman showed that marked specimens of *Littorina rudis* did not change their position on the rocks for thirty-one days. What is more, all the gastropods mentioned are, as a rule, exposed to the blazing rays of the sun; so their capacity to make a minimum of moisture go a long way becomes truly phenomenal.

The future physiologist will find plenty to occupy him in clearing up the secrets of breathing in many gastropods. The land operculate gastropods—which make up several families—are structurally related to the gill breathers, yet they never seek the water; and many species of them live attached to limestone cliffs, where they are not infrequently exposed to the blazing rays of the sun.

All the land and fresh-water mollusks that have no operculum breathe by means of a lung cavity or true lung. These constitute the group known collectively as the Pulmonata. The lung in the Pulmonata is by no means the complex organ of respiration designated by that name in the Mammalia; it is rather a pouch, simple or with complex folds, lined with a mucous membrane which is richly charged with fine blood vessels.

Some gastropods, for example the apple snails (*Ampullaria*), have both gills and lung and can make use of both or either for respiration. On the other hand some of the nudibranchs—marine gastropods which have no shell in the adult stage—have neither gills nor lung, but breathe through the skin.

Nature has contrived no more successful organ for the getting and grinding of food than the tonguelike radula, armed with teeth, which is characteristic of mollusks higher than the Pelecypoda and to which we have already had occasion to refer in discussing the Scaphopoda. The radula is present in all gastropods with the exception of the superfamily Gymnoglossa, some of which live parasitically in starfishes, sea urchins, and their kin and so have no need for a food-capturing organ, while others have a suctorial proboscis to take the place of a radula.

Even when present in gastropods the radula is not always the only organ of mastication. Many species of this class of mollusks have jaws (Fig. 11) with which to bite off and partly crush their food. But the radula usually plays the leading role in food getting and food grinding.

This organ lies upon a thick muscular cushion which is situated on the floor of the snail's mouth (Fig. 12). A tough membrane covers its under surface, and it may bear many rows of fine teeth. The radula in operation has been likened to a cat's tongue when that animal is licking, but its motion is much slower. During feeding the snail can press this organ against the roof of his mouth, or he can advance it to the jaws, or he can even project part of it beyond the jaws. The radula does not bite the food taken into the mouth and thus mince it, but rasps it to pieces as a file rasps iron. Watch almost any fresh-

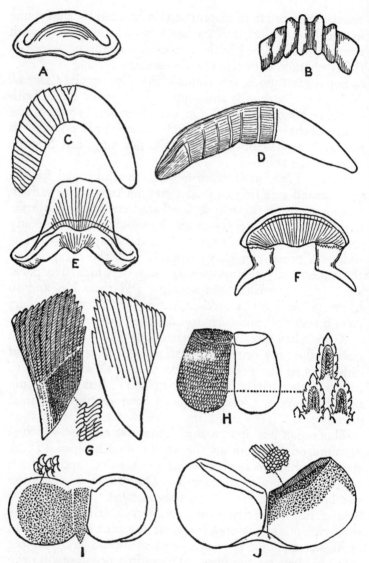

FIG. 11. Jaws of various gastropods to show differences in shape
and structure. All much enlarged. After Cooke

water snail cut a swath through a thin growth of confervae in an aquarium and you will see the operation of the radula.

Great differences occur in the width and length of the radula. In some, like *Littorina*, it is coiled up like a watch

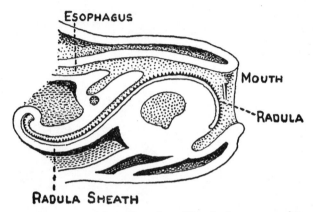

FIG. 12. Longitudinal section of head of a gastropod. After Lang

spring at its posterior extremity and is several times as long as the whole gastropod.

The snail is more fortunate than man, who has to depend on just two sets of teeth to last him through life; the radula is inclosed at its posterior extremity in the radular sheath, and in this sheath new rows of teeth are constantly developing and slowly moving forward to replace the worn-out teeth at the outer end.

Students of mollusks have agreed upon a classification of the radula teeth (Fig. 13). They call the central tooth the rachidian; the tooth (or, perhaps, teeth) on each side of the rachidian the lateral; and that or those beyond the lateral, at each end of the radula, the marginal tooth or teeth. As suggested above, the lateral teeth may occur singly (one on each side of the rachidian tooth) or in a group of several (one group on each side); and the same

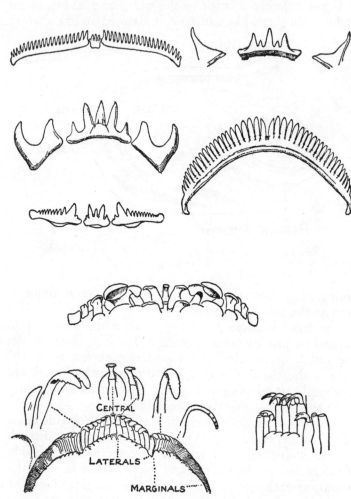

CENTRAL TOOTH WITH THREE CUSPS

CENTRAL

LATERALS

MARGINALS

Fig. 13. Single rows of teeth from the radulas of gastropods, illustrating variety of structure. Much enlarged. After Cooke

[50]

PLATE 20

Opercula of various gastropods, illustrating variety in shape and surfacing

PLATE 21

Cepolis ovumreguli aestivating in a palm leaf

is true of the marginal teeth. A. H. Cooke gives us a very lucid picture of the arrangement of the teeth: "The teeth on the radula are almost invariably disposed in a kind of pattern, exactly like the longitudinal rows of colour in a piece of ribbon, down the centre of which runs a narrow stripe, and every band of colour on one side is repeated in the same relative position on the other side."

The number of teeth on the gastropod radula varies from 1 to possibly 750,000, depending on the species. Again to quote Cooke:

When the teeth are very large, they are usually few in number, when small, they are very numerous. In the carnivorous forms, as a rule, the teeth are comparatively few and powerful, while in the phytophagous genera they are many and small. Large hooked and sickleshaped teeth, sometimes furnished with barbs like an arrowhead, and poison-glands, are characteristic of genera which feed on flesh; vegetable feeders, on the contrary, have the teeth rounded, and blunter at the apex, or, if long and narrow, so slender as to be of comparatively little effect. Genera which are normally vegetarian, but which will, upon occasion, eat flesh, *e.g.*, *Limax* and *Hyalinia*, exhibit a form of teeth intermediate between these two extremes.

That snails' teeth may carry poison glands (Fig. 14) will probably surprise most inhabitants of northern countries, for the family which is thus distinguished is confined to tropical seas. The natives of New Guinea have a wholesome dread of the bite of *Conus*. And well they may, for the poisonous nature of the bite of certain species of this genus is well authenticated, as the following instances noted by Cooke, all of which occurred on certain islands near New Guinea, in the South Pacific, will indicate:

Surgeon Hinde, of the British Royal Navy, saw a native on the island of Matupi (New Britain) who had been bitten by a *Conus*

FIG. 14. A tooth from the radula of *Conus imperialis*, showing barb and poison duct (x 50). After Cooke

geographus and who had at once cut small incisions with a sharp stone all over his arm and shoulder. The blood flowed freely, and the native explained that had he not taken this precaution he would have died.

According to Mr. J. Macgillivray, who, in turn, quotes the natives of Aneityum Island, *Conus textile* (called *intrag* by the natives) spits poison upon its victims from a distance of several inches. Two cases of bites from *C. textile* were brought to this gentleman's notice, one of which terminated fatally after gangrene had set in.

Sir Edward Belcher, when in command of the *Samarang*, was bitten by a *Conus aulicus* at a little island off Ternate, in the Moluccas. As he took the creature out of the water it suddenly exserted its proboscis and inflicted a small, deep, triangular wound, causing a sensation similar to that produced by the burning of phosphorus under the skin. This wound was succeeded by a water-filled vesicle.

The digestive system of gastropods, of which the radula happens to be the most distinctive member, may for convenience be divided into mouth, esophagus, stomach, and intestine. The mouth in different species varies from a mere slit without strongly differentiated lips to a long, strong proboscis.

The radula and other food-getting organs of gastropods are, of course, adapted in each species to the feeding habits of that species. The wide range of the class would indicate a great variety of diets, and actual observation confirms such a surmise. Some of the marine forms, which are more or less sedentary in habit, feed on the minute free-floating life of the sea, as do the oysters and their relatives, and in much the same way: the plankton is strained from the water by the cilia of the gills, which then convey it to the mouth.

J. H. Orton found that *Crepidula*, a marine gastropod, feeds as do pelecypods. The radula in this genus, he says, has changed from a rasping to a grasping organ and is used for conveying the collected food masses to the mouth.

PLATE 22

Coat-of-mail shells, chitons. The plates are overlapping and articulated

PLATE 23

Gastropods in their shells.   After various authors

THE SNAILS AND THEIR ALLIES

While collecting many sedimentary marine gastropods, I have observed that their habitats generally suggest long-continued and undisturbed occupation. The old belief that these creatures were nocturnal in their feeding, moving about for that purpose and returning to their abodes by day, seems far fetched, to say the least. Plankton feeding, coupled with the sedentary habit, seems a much more rational explanation, although, of course, this method of feeding is by no means universal among marine gastropods.

The group popularly known as slugs would appear to include both epicures and gluttons. Cooke says of one species: "*Arion ater*, the great black slug, although normally frugivorous, is unquestionably carnivorous as well, feeding on all sorts of animal matter, whether decaying, freshly killed, or even in a living state. It is frequently noticed feeding on earthworms; kept in captivity, it will eat raw beef; it does not disdain the carcasses of its own dead brethren. . . . Indeed it would seem almost difficult to name anything which *Arion ater* will not eat. . . . A specimen kept two days in captivity was turned out on a newspaper, and commenced at once to devour it." It seems that this specimen was also induced to eat Pears' soap, though with reluctance.

Some species of slugs common to England are most destructive in gardens, feeding entirely on chlorophyll-bearing plants; but others feed exclusively on lichens, a fact which would suggest that not all slugs are the enemies of gardeners, and that while it is a protective measure to eliminate certain species, others should be encouraged.

Slugs betray a fondness for flowers and have been known to exercise considerable ingenuity to reach them in spite of man's precautions. Cooke quotes an observer who actually saw many little slugs suspending themselves by slime threads from the rafters and descending on the spikes of the beautiful orchid *Odontoglossum alexandrae;* and thus many spikes, although thickly wadded round

[53]

with cotton wool (which the slugs could not travel over) and growing in pots surrounded by water, were lost.

But our authority cites the following as perhaps the most singular instance of a liking for a particular food: In a London publishing house, slugs were observed, during a period of nearly twelve months, to have fed almost nightly on the coloring matter in certain book covers; and though the trails were often seen over the shelves, and cabbage and lettuce leaves laid down to tempt the creatures, they continued their depredations with impunity for the time above mentioned.

Slugs will sometimes bite their captors' hands. Cooke records some instances of this:

Mr. Kew relates that a *Limax agrestis*, on being stopped with the finger, while endeavoring to escape from the attack of a large *Arion*, attempted to bite fiercely, the rasping action of its radula being plainly felt. According to the same authority, probably all the slugs will rasp the skin of the finger, if it is held out to them, and continue to do so for a considerable time, without however actually drawing blood. While Mr. Gain was handling a large *Arion ater*, it at once seized one of the folds of skin between the fingers of the hand on which it was placed; after the action of the radula had been allowed to continue for about a minute, the skin was seen to be abraded. Another specimen of *Arion ater*, carried in the hand for a long time enclosed in a dock leaf, began to rasp the skin. The operation was permitted until it became too painful to bear. Examination with a lens showed the skin almost rasped away, and the place remained tender and sore, like a slight burn, for several days.

In order that the reader might connect, in a very general way at least, the structures and functions of mollusks with those of vertebrate animals (with which he is more familiar), we touched upon the nervous and circulatory systems of the Pelecypoda and Scaphopoda in the chapters dealing with these groups. To discuss these systems in the Gastropoda, however, would involve us in too many technicalities. But it may be of special interest to know that malacologists have largely depended on the nervous system to divide the class Gastropoda into two subclasses: Streptoneura and Euthyneura.

THE SNAILS AND THEIR ALLIES

Gastropods display anything but uniformity in their reproductive mechanisms. In the majority of species the sexes are separate, that is, each individual is male or female; but in whole groups of them, such as the Pulmonata, the individual is both male and female. This fact of hermaphroditism results in phenomena which in the higher vertebrates would seem extraordinary. In these hermaphroditic forms mutual impregnation between two individuals may take place; that is, each of the two may function as both male and female at the same time and thus fertilize the other. In most hermaphroditic species, however, one indivdual assumes the role of male and the other that of female during mating. Sometimes a string of *Limnaea* can be seen thus united, each individual serving as male to one and female to the other of its adjacent neighbors.

Several species of *Limnaea* have been known to reproduce parthenogenetically; that is, without mating.

In by far the larger number of gastropod species in which the sexes are distinct it is impossible to discover the sex of an individual by examining its exterior. However, in some species, the opercula, the radula teeth, the feet, or the tentacles differ sufficiently in the two sexes to distinguish them; or the two may differ in size. The female of *Lacuna pallidula*, for example, has ten times the bulk of the male.

Internal fertilization is not the universal rule in gastropods, but depends on the presence of an intrusive organ. Such species as lack this organ cast their sperm into the sea, where the ova are also discharged; and if the sperm comes in contact with the ova, it fertilizes them. Internal fertilization is the rule in all land mollusks.

Another phenomenon sometimes observed in certain gastropods in which the sexes are distinct is that of delayed fertilization; that is, part or all of the quantity of sperm received by the female at any one time may be stored for later use and may even serve to fertilize successive batches of ova developing at widely spaced intervals of time. For such storing of the sperm, some species of Gastropoda have a sperm receptacle connected with the oviduct.

Other organs accessory to the reproductive system that may be present in gastropods of distinct sex are the albumen gland, which furnishes the eggs with food material, and the shell gland, which secretes the covering of the eggs.

But some of the hermaphroditic gastropods have an accessory to the reproductive system of a remarkable sort. This is the dart sac, which contains the love dart— a dart-shaped, tubular shaft of carbonate of lime. This dart, when shot out, is used to inflict punctures and thus produce excitement in mating.

Gastropods, like all other mollusks, reproduce by means of eggs. These eggs may be laid or they may be stored in brood pouches within the parent to undergo further development.

In the manner in which they deposit their eggs and in the number of eggs to a batch, the various species of gastropods show their customary diversity. Thus a single female of the nudibranch genus *Doris* is said to lay from 80,000 to 600,000 eggs to a batch. At the other extreme are the pulmonate land shells: at least, one female of the species *Arion ater* is said to have laid 477 eggs in 480 days. *Helix aspera* lays from 40 to 100 eggs in nests or little hollows at the roots of grass. *Cerion* (Plate 24), a genus of West Indian land mollusks, usually deposits its eggs singly, also at the roots of grass. Many of the Philippine tree snails deposit a single layer of eggs on leaves of the trees they inhabit, whereupon the leaf curls up over the eggs and affords them protection.

The eggs may be deposited singly (Plate 25). In many species, however, they are included in capsules—many eggs to each capsule— and these capsules in turn may be deposited either singly or in groups or chains (Plate 26). Some pelagic species, like *Ianthina* (Fig. 15, lower), make a raft by secreting certain substances that congeal when they come in contact with the water. To the underside of the raft the eggs are then attached. In most marine and

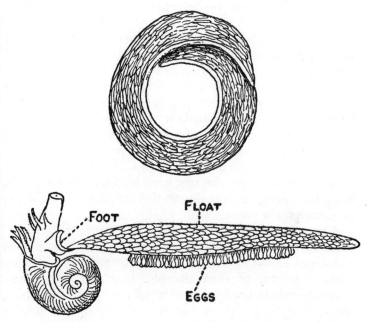

FIG. 15. Upper, spawn of a species of *Natica;* lower, *Ianthina fragilis* and its spawn. After Cooke, and Quoy and Gaimard

fresh-water egg-laying species the egg or capsule is more or less leatherlike; in some of the land forms, however, it is incased in a calcareous test, not unlike that of birds. *Natica* makes a case of sand agglutinated by copious mucus, into which the eggs are dropped (Fig. 15, upper). The sheet curls in a ringlike form.

Development of those species in which the eggs are cast into the sea and there fertilized usually progresses in an orthodox manner; that is, the young animal passes through the several larval stages already discussed in connection with the Pelecypoda. In the land gastropods a syncopation of these stages usually occurs, and the offspring emerges from the egg or brood pouch in a stage far in advance of the larval forms observed in the marine species. The extent of deviation in the various groups is great.

Gastropods obtain their impressions of the external world by one or another of the senses of touch, smell, sight, and hearing. The entire bodily surface of these animals, and especially that of the foot, is sensitive to touch; but they also have a pair of special organs which seem to be devoted exclusively to this sense just as eyes are devoted to sight. I refer to the tentacles, which are such a marked character of the garden snails. When an individual of almost any species of Cuban helicinids is in movement, it keeps the tentacles in constant vibration, thus furnishing a fine illustration of the animal's dependence upon them.

A personal experience will show how acute the sense of smell in snails may be. I once kept a number of individuals of *Limax flavus* in my house for experimental purposes. Several of them escaped from their cage and crawled beneath the flooring through a mouse hole, coming forth at night to forage. In recapturing them I used a boiled potato as bait, and made the discovery that they got the scent of the potato from a distance as great as seventy-six feet. I have also found, in collecting snails in lakes and streams, that by trailing a lump of suet over floating vegetation from different directions toward a common center and leaving the lump anchored in the center for a day all the aquatic snails will head for the suet. It is undoubtedly the sense of smell that guides them in this reaction. In the same way fish traps and lobster pots, baited with dead fish or carrion of any kind, will gather all the marine mollusk flesh eaters in the vicinity.

Moquin-Tandon has established by experiment that the

PLATE 24

Colony of *Cerion casablancae* in a shrub

PLATE 25

Eggs and young of *Strophocheilus ovatus*, natural size

sense of smell in helicid mollusks resides in a little knob at the end of the larger tentacles, close to the eye. He found by removing the tentacle in both *Limax* and *Arion* that these creatures lost their olfactory powers.

In most of the marine gastropods the organ of smell seems intimately associated with the breathing organs.

The achievement of the gastropod individual that has an estimated total of 750,000 teeth in the radula, is approached by a certain *Chiton*, which, it has been esti-

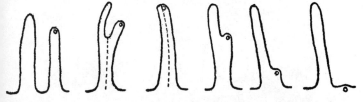

Fig. 16.   Relations of the tactile and optic tentacles in the Prosobranchiata.   After Lang

mated, possesses no less than 12,000 eyes, scattered over the shell. At the other extreme, just as some gastropods have but a single tooth, so there are species with but a single pair of eyes. The various positions that the paired eyes may take in relation to the tentacles are indicated in Figure 16.

The efficiency of vision among snails likewise varies greatly. Some species seem able to do no more than distinguish between light and dark, while other groups have highly specialized eyes. Many experiments and observations have conclusively shown that some of the helicid land mollusks are shortsighted and that they see better in faint than in bright light; this is undoubtedly an adjustment to the crepuscular habits of most of them. It has been determined, for example, that *Helix* can perceive objects better at a distance of six centimeters in dim light than at four or five millimeters in strong light. Some of the operculates, on the other hand, are comparatively longsighted, perceiving objects at distances up to thirty centimeters.

Nearly all species of mollusks have a marked predilection either for or against light. Only one species, so far as known, is indifferent.

Eyes are not always necessary to enable mollusks to "see." Experiments have shown that some can perceive

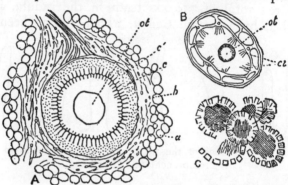

Fig. 17. Otocysts in A, *Anodonta;* B, *Cyclas;* ot, otolith; a, b, c, c', cellular layers surrounding the chamber; cl, cilia on interior walls of chamber. C, an otolith crushed. After Simroth

variation of light by means of the skin alone and will shun or seek the light without eyes just as they do with them. A few marine mollusks, whether with or without eyes, have also been shown to be exceedingly sensitive to the impact of a shadow.

Many marine gastropods, as well as some land forms, are completely without eyes. In some species these organs are usable in the young stages, but they become overgrown with skin and probably rendered functionless. Incidentally, some of these blind land forms that live in earthworm burrows, such as *Caecilianella*, have recently been accused of nipping the roots of sugar cane. The wound thus produced is said to permit the ingress of bacteria that cause the destruction of the cane.

The organs of hearing in the gastropod consist of a pair of otocysts (ear sacs) containing from one to a hundred or more otolites (ear stones) and nerves which transmit perceptions to headquarters for suitable action (Fig. 17). The sacs are located on the pedal ganglia, and have the appearance of two little white points. However, it is the cerebral rather than the pedal ganglia that appear to function as the nerve center for the hearing organs. The otocysts are entirely closed, they are filled with liquid, and their inner surfaces are lined with epithelium bearing innumerable cilia. There are no auditory canals leading in to the ear sacs from the outer world.

The late Dr. Joseph Leidy, to whom we owe much of our knowledge regarding the sense of hearing in gastropods, has the following to say regarding otolites (which in his day were called otoconites): "They vary in size, are oval in form, transparent, composed of concentric layers of carbonate of lime, and frequently have a small cavity in their centre. During life and for a short time after the death of the animal, the otoconites are endowed with a peculiar vibratory movement, by which they are disposed to accumulate into a mass in the centre of the auditory vesicle. After the cessation of the movement, they become diffused through the fluid of the vesicle."

To what extent the gastropods can actually hear is uncertain. Their hearing organs may be only supersensitive organs of touch which feel vibrations that would produce sound if they came into contact with an eardrum. The sensitivity to sound of gastropods may be somewhat like that of deaf persons, who are often aware of vibrations of greater or less intensity which persons of normal hearing recognize as sound—perhaps as faint as the footfall of a mouse, perhaps as loud as a crash of thunder. Whether it be by feeling or by hearing (as we understand that sense) that the gastropods interpret such vibrations, the presence of otolites and of the rest of the apparatus that suggests hearing seems to prove that they need to know what is vibrating about them, as well as to know through their ordinary sense of touch what they come into contact with, what changes take place in temperature and moisture, and other factors of environment.

GASTROPODS IN HUMAN ECONOMY

Gastropods are useful to man in more ways than one; and in our discussion of them from this angle it seems well to consider first their value as food. The abalone, or sea-ear, has already been mentioned as a food mollusk; and the snail may be placed in the same category. For in much of continental Europe, as every one knows, snails are considered a delicacy. Their cultivation for the table is no new thing: Cooke points out that it dates back to the time of the Romans. The several species of the genus *Helix* shown in Plate 27 appear in the markets of France today. Cooke gives the following exceedingly interesting account of the history of snail cultivation:

It was a certain Fulvius Hirpinus who, according to Pliny the elder, first instituted snail preserves at Tarquinium, about 50 B.C. He appears to have bred several species in his "cochlearia," keeping them separate from one another. In one division were the *albulae*, which came from Reate; in another the "very big snails" (probably *H. lucorum*), from Illyria; in a third the African snails, whose characteristic was their fecundity; in a fourth those from Soletum, noted for their "nobility." To increase the size of his snails, Hirpinus fed them on a fattening mixture of meal and new wine, and, says the author in a burst of enthusiasm, "the glory of this art was carried to such an extent that a single snail-shell was capable of holding eighty sixpenny pieces." Varro recommends that the snaileries be surrounded by a ditch, to save the expense of a special slave to catch the runaways. Snails were not regarded by the Romans as a particular luxury. Pliny the younger reproaches his friend Septicius Clarus for breaking a dinner engagement with him, at which the menu was to have been a lettuce, three snails and two eggs apiece, barley water, mead and snow, olives, beetroot, gourds and truffles, and going off somewhere else where he got oysters, scallops, and sea-urchins. In Horace's time they were used as a gentle stimulant to the appetite, for

"'Tis best with roasted shrimps and Afric snails
To rouse your drinker when his vigour fails."

[62]

PLATE 26

Egg capsules of *Busycon carica* and *Buccinum undatum*

PLATE 27

European edible snails (*Helix*)

THE SNAILS AND THEIR ALLIES

Escargotières, or snail-gardens, still exist in many parts of Europe, e.g., at Dijon, at Troyes and many other places in central and southern France, at Brunswick, Copenhagen, and Ulm. The markets at Paris, Marseilles, Bordeaux, Toulouse, Nantes, etc., are chiefly supplied by snails gathered from the open country, and particularly from the vineyards, in some of which *Helix pomatia* abounds. In the *Morning Post* of 8th May, 1868, there is an account of the operation of clearing the celebrated Clos de Vougeot vineyard of these creatures. No less than 240 gallons were captured, at a cost in labour of over 100 francs, it being estimated that these snails would have damaged the vines to an extent represented by the value of fifteen to twenty pipes of wine against which may be set the price fetched by the snails when sold in the market.

According to Dr. Gray, the glassmen at Newcastle used to indulge in a snail feast once a year, and a recent writer informs us that *H. aspersa* is still eaten by working people in the vicinity of Pontefract and Knottlingley. But in this country [England] snails appear to be seldom consciously used as an article of food; the limitation is necessary, for Lovell tells us that they are much employed in the manufacture of cream, and that a retired (!) milkman pronounced it the most successful imitation known.

Gastropods, as well as some pelecypods, are valuable, also, for their shells. Even among modern peoples the shells of certain species have attracted much attention and have had an extraordinary value as curiosities. A century ago, more or less, when public museums with their treasures were not the common institutions they are today, many persons made private collections of natural-history objects of various kinds. In such collections mollusk shells, because of their beauty of form and color, held a prominent place. Certain specimens have brought almost fabulous prices—just how much depending on how nearly perfect they were and how rare. In 1854, in London, a single shell (*Conus gloriamaris*) brought £43 1s. (roughly $215); while at the end of the century a *Pleurotomaria adansoniana* was offered for sale for about £100 ($500).

Many primitive peoples and some not so primitive have used snail shells as currency. Until the end of the last century cowrie shells were an accepted medium of exchange among the natives of British India. About four thousand shells in good condition are said to have passed for a shilling.

As sources of dyes and inks, mollusks—and particularly gastropods—rank high. The classic source of mollusk dyes is the purple shell, a gastropod which malacologists have recently transferred from the genus *Purpura* to the genus *Murex*. The purple shell contributed the Tyrian purple of antiquity. George W. Tryon, in his *Manual of Conchology*, relates how, according to tradition, this dye first became known. It appears that the dog of a Tyrian nymph crushed some of the mollusks now known as *Murex trunculus* in his teeth, thus staining his mouth purple. The color was so beautiful that the fair nymph expressed to her lover, Hercules, her desire to have a robe of similar hue. Hercules, of course, gratified her, and thus began the use of the mollusk dye.

The Indians of the New World also understood how to extract purple dye from shellfish.

To produce the finest Tyrian purple it is evident that the ancients mixed the dye products obtained from two different species: Pliny gives the proportion of 200 pounds of juice of "Buccinum" and 111 pounds of that of "Pelagia" as suitable for obtaining a beautiful amethyst color, sufficient for fifty pounds of wool. To quote from Mr. Tryon:

The extent of the Tyrian industry is visible in numerous holes in the rocks, two to three feet deep, containing the breccia of shells anciently crushed in them for the extraction of the dye. The arms of the city as preserved on its medals were the *Purpura* shell, and in the time of Strabo the multiplicity of dye-works unpleasantly affected the air of the vicinity.

The Romans used various species in great quantity for dyeing purposes, and the remains of Murices form vast heaps; indeed, in one case, at Tarento, the mass is so large as to have received the name of "Monte Testaceo." The color was prepared by pounding up small specimens, or by breaking the shells of larger ones and extracting the purple gland. This fluid was mixed with five or six times its weight of water, with twenty ounces of soda to every hundred pounds. Placed in lead or tin vessels the mixture was exposed to the sun for several days, until the hue desired was obtained, when the wool was simply plunged into it and allowed to remain for a few hours. Under Augustus the dyed wool brought as much as $200 per pound.

It is no wonder that the production of purple dye became a thriving industry among the Romans and remained so until a law was passed which prohibited the wearing of purple to any but the imperial family. This was the deathblow of this industry, which thenceforth rapidly declined and died out so completely that during the Middle Ages the very existence of such a dye was considered fabulous. With the Renaissance, however, when the arts and civilization of the ancients were revived, the method of producing it was rediscovered and for a while successfully practiced. Chemistry, however, has now supplied the world with even more brilliant colors, and this at a great saving in producing the dye.

When we come to consider the ink- or dye-secreting ability of certain mollusks we find inseparably associated with it their ability to throw a "smoke" screen about themselves, using the ink as the "smoke" of the screen. And here the mollusks assume a new significance. For the smoke screen has become a definite part of the defense mechanism of modern warfare, especially by sea; and man may well have copied this idea from the mollusks. A number of species have the power, when annoyed, of throwing out secretions which serve to repel the assailant or produce a screen behind which the fugitive may retreat to safety. If man did copy the idea from the mollusks, he is doubly indebted to them on this count; for, as we have already told, he has long made use, as dye or ink, of the substance they eject to form their screens.

The classic examples of smoke screening among the mollusks are furnished by the squids and octopuses that secrete the original "India ink." These mollusks belong to the order Cephalopoda. But there are screen throwers among the Gastropoda, also. The members of the family Aplysiidae, which include the "sea hares," can eject a purple liquid in sufficient quantity—as I have observed in Philippine, West Indian, and Mexican waters—to so discolor a tub of water as to hide the animal completely. Another gastropod screen thrower is the little pelagic violet snail *Ianthina*, which, when disturbed, exudes a protective cloud of violet ink. *Ianthina* plays a leading role in an amusing story which Doctor Simpson, one of our veteran malacologists, tells on himself. Once while serving in the Navy, Doctor Simpson went on shore all decked out in white. So arrayed he came unexpectedly upon a stranded colony of *Ianthina*, and in his enthusiasm he filled all his pockets with them. But a clammy feeling soon dampened his enthusiasm, and he looked down to find his fine white suit streaked with violet where the ianthinas had discharged their ink. Our indefatigable collector had changed color to such an extent that he had to remain in hiding until nightfall, when, under cover of the darkness, he returned to his ship.

But these various relations of gastropods to man (other than as food) are secondary and incidental when compared to their relation to him as carriers of harmful germs. As contributors to human diseases they loom large on the horizon of millions of people. Mollusks do not attack man directly, but serve as essential intermediate hosts to a number of man's death-dealing enemies; that is, these enemies, called flukes, must find a mollusk in which to pass certain stages of development or else they die. All trematode flat worms (class Trematoda) are believed to require a mollusk as an intermediate host in which to undergo a part of their development. There is an endless variety of these worms, and our knowledge leads us to believe that probably all species of vertebrates entertain within their bodies one or more kinds of them.

Man is no exception to this rule, but is rather unusually plagued with trematodes. The cosmopolitan habitat of man has attracted to him the parasites of all the world.

At least he enjoys the distinction of having more kinds of them than are known in any other one species of animal.

To understand the role played by mollusks in undermining human health, we must know something of the life cycle of a fluke. To describe this cycle I shall select as a concrete example the best known and most studied species—*Fasciola hepatica*, even though it is one of the least important flukes so far as its direct effect upon human health is concerned. Indirectly it does affect man's interests, however, since at the present time it is held responsible for the destruction annually in the United States of about twenty million dollars' worth of sheep livers.

The adult worm normally resides in the sheep's liver. The eggs pass into the bile passages, then through the bile duct into the intestines, from which they are eliminated with the feces. To hatch they must be immersed in fresh water; and this takes place if the feces happen to be dropped into a pool or stream or if the eggs are washed there by rain. The larva, slipping from the egg, is covered with a ciliated coat by means of which it is able to swim in quest of a mollusk. In America the snail usually chosen is *Stagnicola bulimoides* or one of its subspecies. The larva enters the tissues of the mollusk and loses its cilia. Thereafter, the larva goes through a series of changes until it transforms into not one but many tadpolelike cercaria, which worm their way out of the molluscan host. The tail of the larval fluke aids it to swim to some blade of grass, where it encysts. Sheep, browsing along the water's edge, ingest the grass and likewise the flukes which thus reach the alimentary tract of the definitive host. From this they migrate to the host's liver, where they develop their adult characteristics, and thus complete their life cycle. Some of the cercaria may also be swallowed by the sheep when they are drinking water in which the flukes have been set free. Figure 18 illustrates the life cycle of the fluke.

If for any reason the larva fails to find its intermediate molluscan host, it dies, and this fact has caused man to look for relief from trematode infestation by eliminating

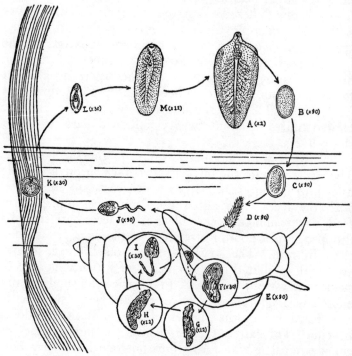

FIG. 18.   Diagrammatic representation of the life history of a fluke (*Fasciola hepatica*). A, adult worm in sheep's liver; B, C, egg; D, miracidium, the newly hatched larva in water; E-H, redia and sporocysts—developmental stages in a mollusk; I, cercarian; J, free-swimming cercarian; K, larva encysted on a blade of grass; L, M, development within sheep.   After Chandler

the intermediate host and thus preventing development, rather than by medication of infested individuals, only to have them subject to continued attacks. The flukes that infest man may be found in his blood, lungs, liver, or alimentary tract.

THE SNAILS AND THEIR ALLIES

The following table lists many of the best known flukes, their intermediate hosts, and their mammalian definitive hosts.

Fluke	Geographical distribution	Molluscan intermediate host	Mammalian definitive host
BLOOD FLUKES: *Schistosoma japonica*	Japan China	*Katayama Oncomelania*	Man
Schistosoma hematobium	Southern Europe Africa Mauritius	*Planorbis Physopsis Bulinus Melania*	Man
Schistosoma mansoni	Africa South America West Indies	*Physopsis Ampullaria Planorbis*	Man Monkey
Schistosoma spindale	Sumatra India South Africa	*Planorbis*	Man Cattle
Schistosoma bovis	Sicily Africa	*Physopsis*	Man Cattle
LUNG FLUKES: *Paragonimus ringeri*	Japan Philippines Korea China	*Melania*	Man Dog Cat Swine and others
LIVER FLUKES: *Fasciola hepatica* *Fasciola gigantea*	World-wide	*Lymnaea*	Man Sheep Goat Cattle Swine Cat Dog Fox
Clonorchis sinensis	Japan Korea to French Indo-China	*Parafossarulus Bythinia*	Man Cat Dog Swine

MOLLUSKS

Fluke	Geographical distribution	Molluscan intermediate host	Mammalian definitive host
LIVER FLUKES: *Dicrocoelium dendriticum*	Europe Africa Asia North America South America	Unknown	Man Herbivores Omnivores
INTESTINAL FLUKES: *Watsonius watsoni*	Africa	Unknown	Man
Gastrodicus hominis	French Indo-China	Unknown	Man
Fasciolopsis buski	From Formosa through China to India	*Hippeutis Segmentina*	Man Swine Dog
Heterophyes heterophyes	Japan China Egypt	Unknown	Man Dog Cat
Metagonimus yokogawi	Japan	*Brotia*	Man
Amphimerus noverca	India	Unknown	Man
Fascioletta ilocana	Philippines	Unknown	Man
Echinostoma revoltum	Europe	Unknown	Man
Echinostoma malayanum	Malacca	Unknown	Man
Artyfechinostomum sufrartyfex	Assam	Unknown	Man

CHAPTER V

THE OCTOPUSES, SQUIDS, AND THEIR KIN

In the squid, octopus, nautilus, and their relatives, which together constitute the class Cephalopoda, we meet a group which has about it the aura of legend rather than the sober tone of reality. The octopus and its misdeeds share fame and fascination with such legendary beasts as the Minotaur and the sea-serpent (which may in fact be a giant squid's tentacle). Seizing on strange reports of sailormen, story-tellers from Pliny to Jules Verne have dealt freely with a basis of fact sufficiently bizarre in itself.

For there is actually much to excite wonder in these animals—their size, strength, ferocity, and cunning; their beauty, grace, and speed. They are truly the stuff of which legends are made. Even the student of natural history finds them something of an anomaly, so far superior in organization are they to all the other Mollusca.

It may be that the key to the comparatively high nervous development of the octopus and squid can be found in their loss of an external shell. Certainly the only modern cephalopod that retains this shell housing—the chambered nautilus—is a stupid animal as compared with all his shell-less relatives. It is easy to see how release from the confines of a shell would open up new possibilities for bodily development; it is almost equally evident that this bodily development, resulting in increased speed and agility, would bring about an increase of brain power, just as the development in man of that extraordinary tool, the apposable thumb, led to brain expansion.

A shell is, of course, a fortress securing safety to its possessor without mental effort; but when the fortress is taken away a species must compensate for it by greater agility, strength, or keenness, or else submit to extinction. Finally, the energy released from shell-making might very well have gone, in part, into brain formation.

Paleontology teaches us that the cephalopods can boast of a long line of progenitors; indeed, in this respect there are few groups that can compare with them. Millions upon millions of years ago, in Upper Cambrian times, there existed in the seas a small nautiloid animal whose remains contributed to the formation of what is known as the Chau-mi-tien limestone near Tsi-nan, Shantung, China. Its shell is only seven millimeters in length and three millimeters in diameter (Fig. 19, A). This tiny, flexed but noncoiled, chambered nautiloid ancestor of the Cephalopoda (which Dr. Charles D. Walcott has christened *Cyrtoceras cambria*) is ancient enough surely. But it must certainly have been preceded by a long line of other chambered nautiluses; and the order has continued uninterruptedly ever since. The Ozarkian period ushered in a number of families, each with its genera and species. The Canadian period added materially to these; but the greatest differentiation of all took place in the Ordovician and Silurian periods, after which the decline of the order began. This has now reached the point where only four, closely allied species, belonging to the single genus *Nautilus* remain. They all inhabit rather shallow water about the shores and coral reefs of the South Pacific. They seem to cling to the bottom, creeping about there all their lives and never coming to the surface voluntarily. About three thousand extinct species of the suborder Nautiloidea have been named up to the present time, and to this number new forms are constantly being added by the patient paleontologist.

In all the nautiloids the shell is divided into chambers by transverse concave septa, whose margins may be straight or undulate; a siphuncle, or tube, connects the chambers (Plate 28). The variation in shape and size of nautiloid shells is great. They range from straight to closely coiled cones (Fig. 19, B and C). The shell sculpture, too, presents no end of variations. Whatever the sculpture or size, which varies from the seven-millimeter ancestor to the fourteen-foot cones of *Endoceras*, I have yet to see a nautiloid shell that lacks elegance.

During the Upper Silurian period a new offshoot of the cephalopod stock developed, an offshoot which soon far excelled the Nautiloidea in number of individuals as well as in diversity of structure. This is the suborder Ammonoidea, (so called because of their horns), of which probably more than six thousand species are known (Fig. 19, D, E, and F). In them form, complexity of septation, and external sculpture ran riot and attained an overspecialization which soon spelled exit; for the group reached its highest development in the Upper Triassic and disappeared suddenly and completely at the close of the Cretaceous. In size the ammonoid shells vary from the dimensions of a pea to more than six feet in diameter.

The Nautiloidea and the Ammonoidea belong to the order Tetrabranchiata, and are distinguished by having, as the name implies, four gills. All other cephalopods— and this means all living forms of this class except the four species of *Nautilus*—belong to the order Dibranchiata, the members of which have two gills. The dibranchs are a much younger offshoot of the cephalopod tribe than are the tetrabranchs dating back to the Triassic only, at which time the belemnoids first appeared on the scene.

Evidently it is among the belemnoids that we must seek the ancestors of the squids and cuttlefishes; for the belemnoids were the first cephalopods to have an internal shell, though it was of much greater complexity than is the internal shell of the modern animals (Fig. 20, A). The belemnoids also possessed an ink bag, a character

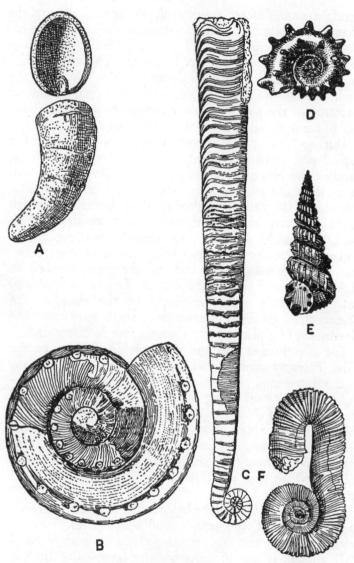

FIG. 19. Fossil cephalopods. A, *Cyrtoceras cambria*, end and side views; B, C, nautiloids; D-F, ammonoids

present in almost all recent dibranchiate cephalopods, but absent in the tetrabranchs. It is quite possible that the belemnoids were as abundant in the seas of their time as their ancestors had been before them and as their descendants are today; but so little fossilizable material did their bodies contain that scarcely anything remained of them after death, and the rocks contain only a meager, scattered, and fragmentary record of their existence.

The belemnoids are the most recent of fossil cephalopods and are followed directly by the modern dibranchs, which include the great majority of the class now found in the seas. As already noted, all living cephalopods fall into the following subdivisions:

Class Cephalopoda
   I. Order Tetrabranchiata
      (contains only one living genus, *Nautilus*, the only cephalopod which still has an inclosing shell)
  II. Order Dibranchiata
      1. Suborder Decapoda
         (contains squids and cuttlefishes)
      2. Suborder Octopoda
         (contains octopuses)

All the tetrabranchs, living and extinct, possess in common at least one invariable character—an external shell. This character has never appeared in any of the dibranchs, all the members of this order, whether living or extinct, possessing either an internal skeleton or none at all. In the squids the shell is embedded in the dorsal part of the mantle and frequently reduced to a mere chitinoid remnant, called the pen (Fig. 20, B–D), from its resemblance to the quill pens of old. In the cuttlefishes the shell remnant is strongly reinforced with calcareous material (Fig. 20, E). It constitutes the cuttle bone of commerce, which is generally considered an indispensable adjunct to a bird cage. The only coiled or chambered shell is found in the decapod *Spirula* (Fig. 20, F); but, like the shells of all the other dibranchs, that of *Spirula* is internal, being contained within the mantle. The shell of the beautiful paper nautilus—the octopod *Argonauta* (which must not be confused with the tetrabranch chambered nautilus discussed above)—is not a skeletal shell

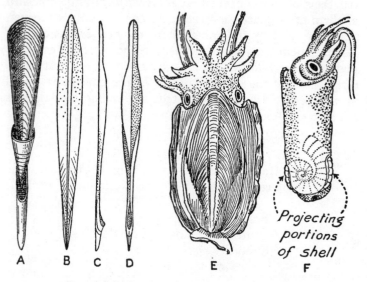

FIG. 20. Internal shells of cephalopods. A, pen of a fossil belemnoid, restored; B, pen of a squid; C, D, pen of a squid from the front and side; E, cuttlefish with mantle removed to show shell; F, *Spirula*. After various authors

at all, but only a case used by the female for the protection of her eggs. Finally, in the octopus the shell has degeneraated into two chitinous rods.

Thus degeneration has been the fate of the molluscan shell in the dibranch cephalopods. These animals have, however, compensated in part for their loss by the acquisition of a cartilaginous skeleton, the tissue of which is very like the hyaline cartilage of vertebrates. This skeleton is but one of the many characters in which cephalopods approach the vertebrates more nearly than do any other of the invertebrate animals.

The cartilaginous skeleton includes a special box or case for the brain (the braincase) and thus protects that organ; it protects the sense organs also and serves as an attachment for the muscles. So relatively slight is it and so slight are the support and leverage it gives to the muscles that we may well wonder at the beautiful balance of the musculature of the arms. For each arm may be as long and as powerful as a boa constrictor's body—and perhaps more efficient—although it has no bony or cartilaginous support within it, while the boa possesses a complete skeletal framework.

For purposes of description the dibranch body may be divided into the four regions which stand out to the eye of even the casual observer: head, arms, funnel, and trunk or visceral dome. We can speak of a head in these cephalopods with impunity, for this section of the body is well defined and sharply differentiated from the rest. The anterior part of the head, however, is hidden behind the bases of the arms, so that only the posterior portion can be seen externally. Laterally it bears the eyes, which in some forms are stalked, in most sessile, but are prominent in all. The mouth is in the section hidden by the bases of the arms.

Cephalopoda means "headfooted," a term which is certainly an apt one to describe the fringe of arms or tentacles which surround the head in all members of the class. These processes are modifications of the molluscan foot. In the chambered nautilus they are lobelike prolongations of the margin of the head and they bear tentacles—sixty in the male and ninety in the female. The tentacles do not bear suckers; but they are prehensile and adhesive, and each has a sheath into which it may be withdrawn.

The character by which Octopoda and Decapoda are superficially differentiated is indicated in their names:

"eight-footed" and "ten-footed." Unlike *Nautilus*, the dibranch foot is modified into eight or ten muscular, sucker-bearing appendages, or arms. In addition to the four pairs of arms common to both the Octopoda and Decapoda—called the primary arms—the Decapoda have a fifth pair, called the tentacular arms. These are much longer than the other arms and in many species are inserted into pits,

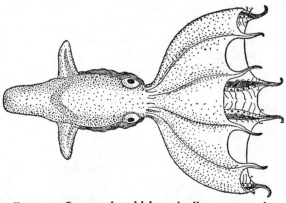

Fig. 21. Octopus in which umbrella connects the arms for their entire length. After Verrill

into which they may be withdrawn. The decapod's fifth pair of arms differs from his four primary pairs in having suckers only at the free, club-shaped end, whereas the primary arms bear suckers along the whole length of their inner surface.

Although the grasping, adhesive, powerful, and versatile processes that surround the head of a dibranchiate cephalopod are the animal's creeping mechanism, the term *arms* describes them better than does the term *feet*. The Octopoda use these processes for creeping more than do the Decapoda, for the Octopoda are principally shore- or bottom-living forms. When the octopod is creeping its body is raised, its head up, its trunk dropped back, and it pulls itself forward chiefly by the contraction of the extended arms. Usually octopods move on the middle sec-

PLATE 28

Shell of the chambered nautilus; external view and cross section to show septa

tions of the arms and carry the tips curled up, but they have been seen to advance on the tips, "toe-dancing" along, as it were, in a graceful, airy fashion.

In certain species of Octopoda some of the arms are united at their bases by a membrane, or web; in others, all of the arms are so united; *Eledone* uses this web as a parachute to let itself gently down to the sea bottom. In

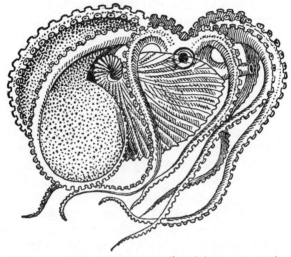

FIG. 22. Female paper nautilus (*Argonauta argo*) swimming. Note the egg case. After Sedgwick

still other octopods—notably *Alloposus* and *Cirroteuthis*— a membrane unites all the arms along their entire length, so that the web with its supporting arms becomes a veritable umbrella, which these genera use in swimming, alternately contracting and expanding it as they move along (Fig. 21).

In another member of the Octopoda, *Argonauta*, the paper nautilus, the terminal parts of the two dorsal arms of the female are expanded into thin membranes, which secrete the shell or egg case (Fig. 22).

In the male of all dibranchs, one of the arms is usually modified for the transfer of sperm to the female. In

some species this arm or part of it becomes detached from
the male in mating and is left in the mantle cavity of the
female. Cuvier, who first described such a detached arm,
mistook it for a parasitic worm and called it *Hectocotylus*.
In consequence, the modified arm of all dibranchs is said
to be hectocotylized.

The loss of an arm does not mean permanent em-
barrassment to a cephalopod; for all members of the class
have power to regenerate injured arms, just as crustaceans
can grow a new claw and lizards a new tail to replace one
broken off.

The suckers that line the inner surfaces of the arms
are what make the arms of Dibranchiata such powerful
grasping organs. There are about eighty suckers on each
arm of an average *Eledone*, the largest of which will
measure three-quarters of an inch in diameter at the rim.
The suckers are sessile in the Octopoda but are stalked
and terminate in a horny ring in the Decapoda. When
the animal wishes to attach its suckers to an object, the
floor of the pit in each sucker is raised while the rim is
applied to the object, and then muscular action withdraws
the floor of the pit so that a vacuum is created. So powerful is the hold of these suckers that one tentacle alone
clinging to a man's hand gives sufficient support to enable
a twenty-inch *Eledone* to hang on while it is withdrawn
bodily from the water. Whales have been taken with
great circular scars in their flesh, made by the suckers of a
giant squid in some fierce battle of the seas. Prey of
ordinary size must be completely helpless in the clutch
of these dibranch suckers.

In certain forms among the dibranchs the suckers on
parts of the arms may be replaced by hooks (see Fig. 30,
page 94). Also, in many of the Decapoda the outer ring
is toothed (Fig. 23).

The cephalopod's chief organ of locomotion—called the
funnel—is, like the arm, a modified portion of the molluscan foot. It can be seen attached to the ventral surface

of the cephalopod's head. In *Nautilus* it consists of two lobes rolled round one another to form a tube; but in the dibranchs the edges of these lobes are fused. In the adaptation of the funnel to swimming, nature has again constructed a locomotive machine fit to serve man as a model for his efforts in this direction. Indeed the "rocket" cars,

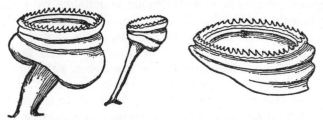

Fig. 23. Suckers of the giant squid with toothed outer rings. The figure on the right is an inch and three-quarters across the rim. Reduced

at present in the experimental stage in Germany, are operated on the principle exemplified in the swimming mechanism of the octopus and his kin. The working of this mechanism may be briefly described as follows: Behind the cephalopod's funnel is the mantle cavity, into which the funnel opens. The cephalopod takes water into this cavity, after which he closes the entry thereto by a special contrivance. Then, by the powerful contraction of the mantle muscles, he forces the water out through the funnel, and the recoils from repetitions of this action drive him backward in rapid jerks. In swimming the cephalopod assumes a position in which the apex of the trunk is in advance of the rest of his body, while the arms trail out behind. The powerful Decapoda, which, unlike the sedentary Octopoda, roam the seas as freely as the whales, swim with great speed and accordingly have a more specialized funnel than the eight-armed group.

All the waste products of the cephalopod's body, as well as the ova and the contents of the ink sac, are eliminated from the mantle cavity through the funnel.

[81]

MOLLUSKS

One structure ties the cephalopods anatomically to the bivalves, snails, and all other mollusks—the mantle. This structure forms the soft but tough integument that incloses the trunk of dibranchs like a bag, and terminates posteriorly at the neck in a lip, which opens into the mantle cavity. The shape of this bag varies with the species and may be globular, conic, spindlelike, cylindrical, or lancelike. Furthermore, in one individual the shape may vary to conform to the activity of the animal. Thus the bluntly rounded sac of an *Eledone* at rest becomes stretched out somewhat like the fuselage of a racing plane when the animal is swimming. At the same time a lateral fold of skin becomes prominent and forms a delicate fin, which undoubtedly helps to support the moving body. With the return to rest, the fin again becomes indistinguishable from the body surface.

Many of the powerfully swimming Decapoda have such lateral flukes strongly developed and permanently visible. However, the most curious modification of the mantle sac is undoubtedly seen in *Spirula*, in which it forms a sucker.

The important part the mantle cavity plays in the swimming mechanism of cephalopods has already been mentioned. This cavity is deep and spacious and contains the gills (four in the *Nautilus*, two in the dibranchs), the anus, the ink sac, the paired kidney openings, and the genital duct. To maintain a fresh supply of water flowing over the comblike gills and to expel the excrementitious matter through the funnel the mantle muscles contract regularly.

Judging from observations made on a specimen of *Eledone* in an aquarium, there appears to be no constant rate of breathing in cephalopods. The rate fell as low as six respirations a minute when the animal was in repose and rose to sixteen a minute when it was agitated. A female *Octopus vulgaris* has been observed to breathe thirty-four times a minute while watching over her eggs.

THE OCTOPUSES, SQUIDS, AND THEIR KIN

So much for the general make-up of cephalopods as seen from the exterior. It is not so easy to give a comprehensive picture of their internal anatomy without lapsing into technicalities. However, the very interesting feeding habits of cephalopods furnish a favorable introduction to an account of their digestive system.

All the Cephalopoda are carnivorous—a fact which has contributed materially to their fearsome reputation. Many forms appear to subsist principally on crustacean food, though they prey on many other kinds of animals, also, including other mollusks, and when more than ordinarily hungry they have no inhibitions to restrain them from cannibalism. Probably no animal of available size in the seas is safe from one species or another of this class, whereas their own ferocity, speed, and strength render the cephalopods, when adult, immune to all but a few enemies.

The dibranchs display remarkable intelligence in the capture of their food. A cuttlefish has been seen to stalk a prawn until within striking distance, when he would shoot out his two long tentacles and grasp his victim, transferring him instantly to the suckers of the shorter arms. Octopuses will creep along in the wake of scuttling crabs or swim after them until they can conveniently drop on them from above. The prey is rendered immediately helpless by the spreading arms of the cephalopod. Sometimes an octopus will capture several crabs in rapid succession, holding those already caught helpless in its suckers while pursuing the others.

The shrift of a crab after capture by a cephalopod is short. The crustacean's legs are torn away, the carapace is lifted—probably by the mollusk's beak—and the body consumed from the ventral side.

Octopus vulgaris feeds chiefly on mussels. These he collects in his nest in groups of fifteen or twenty and then eats. Presumably he opens a mussel by attaching some

[83]

of his suckers to the two valves of the shell and then applying pressure until the valves give way.

The arms transfer the food to the mouth, which is within the circle of arms and is itself circular in shape. The entrance to the mouth is surrounded by a lip and is armed—just inside the lip—with two powerful chitinous jaws, whose shape curiously resembles that of a parrot's beak reversed; that is, the lower or ventral jaw (which is the larger) protrudes beyond the upper and in the act of biting works outside the upper (Fig. 24). These jaws bite vertically with great force, tearing up the food as it is held by the suckers.

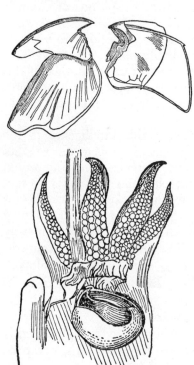

Inside the cephalopod's jaws we meet again that typically molluscan organ, the radula—a broad, toothed, chitinous ribbon lying on the upper surface of the tongue. The tongue supplies the energy which moves the radula back and forth, imparting a rasping action to the structure. The teeth of the radula are large; each row usually bears a central or rachidian tooth and from two to four lateral teeth, depending on the species. This organ further grinds the food cut up by the jaws and passes it on through the esophagus

FIG. 24. Jaws of cephalopods. Upper, jaws of the giant squid; lower, jaws of *Sepia* in place and closed, several of the arms having been cut away. After Cooke

COLOR PLATES

Color effects in the shells of marine gastropods. The beautiful shell
of Number 6 (*Oliva porphyria*) is always hidden, in life, by an even
more beautiful mantle

PLATE B

Ornate bivalve shells from the Gulf of California. The species represented is *Spondylus princeps*

PLATE C

Shells of Hawaiian tree snails (*Achatinella*), showing the varied color patterns which occur in different species of this genus

PLATE D

Shells of Philippine tree snails (*Cochlostyla*), showing variations in color pattern, size, and shape which occur in different species of this genus

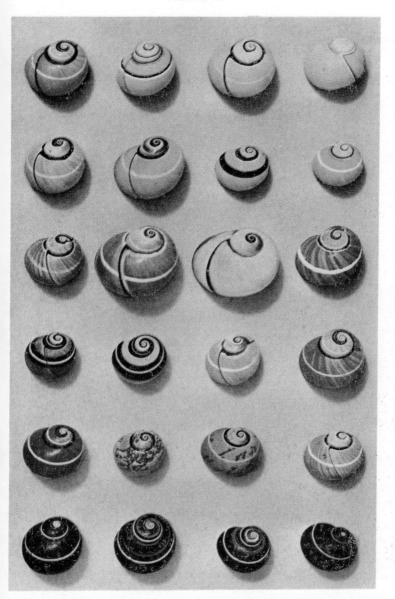

Shells of Cuban land snails (*Polymita*), showing the varied color patterns which occur in different species of this genus

A few of the typical color phases exhibited by *Octopus vulgaris*. Above, a
irritated animal discharging ink; middle, swimming animals; below, a frightene
animal. Modified from Cowdry

to the well-developed stomach, various glands pouring their digestive secretions over it during the passage. The stomach, in *Eledone* at least, is a muscular grinding organ suggestive of a bird's gizzard.

Digestion is completed in the intestine with the aid of other secretions; and the waste products are then passed to the anus, which, as has been stated, opens into the mantle cavity. From here they are expelled through the funnel.

In all living cephalopods except *Nautilus* and *Cirroteuthis* there is a gland opening into the anus which secretes ink—a thick, dark-brown liquid, a few drops of which will color a large volume of water. Adult octopuses generally throw out the ink screen when at rest and then attempt to escape behind it; but they may discharge it while swimming, and more than once. The gland constantly secretes ink, which is stored in a reservoir upon which the cephalopod can draw at will. The ink contains both copper and iron extracted from the blood. Man has long collected this ink, particularly the sepia of cuttlefishes, and used it as a water color.

The higher organization of cephalopods renders inevitable their possession of a more complete circulatory and nervous system than occurs in the other mollusks. Their possession of a cartilaginous protection for the great nerve centers in the head has already been referred to. It is scarcely a misuse of words to call this a braincase and its contents a brain.

The sense organs, which supply impressions to the brain include tactile organs, well-developed eyes, organs of equilibration (the statocysts), olfactory organs (which probably function also as taste organs), and perhaps heat-sensory organs.

The surface of the body of dibranchs is, as a whole, sensitive to touch; although tactile sensibility is specially localized in the arms, as it is in the tentacles of the tetrabranch *Nautilus*.

[85]

MOLLUSKS

Nautilus has simple eyes built on the principle of the pinhole camera, having a sensitive membrane in a dark chamber and a minute hole for the entrance of light; but in all the other members of the Cephalopoda the eyes are large and extremely complicated in structure. In large specimens of *Eledone* the diameter of the eye may be as great as an inch, and there is a record of an eye aperture in a giant squid seven inches wide by nine long. The eyeball is protected by plates of cartilage. Within it are two chambers, a cornea, biconvex lens (which separates the chambers), a highly pigmented iris (which encircles the lens), and a highly innervated and deeply pigmented retina. The complex arrangement of the optic nerve known as the optic chiasma has already been discussed.

Eyes of such complex structure must be efficient organs of vision, and observation has shown that those of some species of cephalopods are more powerful and better adjusted than are the eyes of some vertebrates. Miss Isgrove remarks that "*Eledone*, apparently, dislikes a strong light, in which it seems quite incapable of opening its eyes. If a light is brought near during the night, the eye contracts and the animal retreats."

On the sides of the head, in the cephalopods, one below each eye, are located what are considered to be organs of smell. They may be either hollow tubercles or pits and are supplied with sensory epithelium and innervated by a nerve from the frontal lobes of the cerebral ganglion. There is no direct evidence, however, that these organs are olfactory.

The organs by which cephalopods maintain their equilibrium—statocysts—are paired also. In the *Nautilus* they are located in the head, outside the hard brain cartilage, while in the Dibranchiata they are completely embedded in this cartilage. These statocysts are innervated by nerves from the cerebral ganglion, and in the *Nautilus* each contains numerous small calcareous granules, while in the Dibranchiata a single otolith is present.

PLATE 29

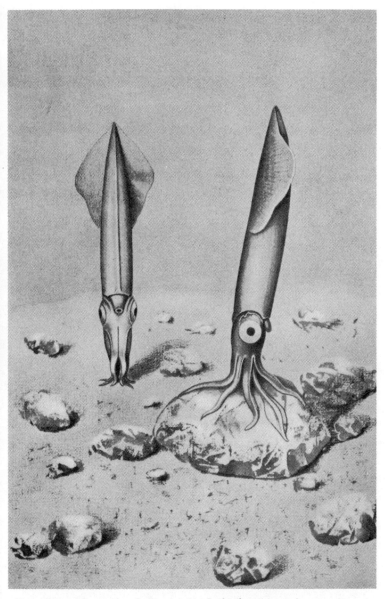

Deposition of eggs by *Loligo pealii*. Left, female moving on tips of arms just before selecting spot for deposition; right, female in act of pressing egg mass on rock. Modified from Drew

PLATE 30

Egg case of paper nautilus (*Argonauta argo*), showing eggs within

Finally, certain Cephalopoda have scattered over the skin some rather singular structures or organs whose use is not surely known (Fig. 25). These structures are highly pigmented and are provided with nerve endings surrounded by transparent cells, so that they look somewhat like tiny eyes. It is thought that they are sensitive to changes in temperature, for which reason they are usually called thermoscopic eyes.

In their reproductive organs and habits the dibranchiate Cephalopoda present some features which are, like so much else about them, unique in the animal kingdom.

In all members of the class the sexes are always separate, and usually the male is smaller than the female. In *Argonauta*, for example, the female may be fifteen times the length of the male. It is in this genus, also, that the female secretes a shell, spiral in shape, in which to carry her eggs.

Of other external characters differentiating the sexes in dibranchs the most reliable is undoubtedly the hectocotylized arm of the male. Hectocotylization is the name given to the special modification of one arm,

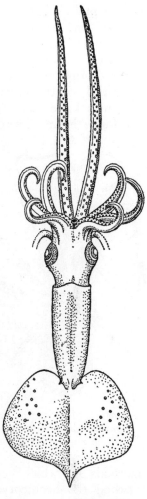

FIG. 25. *Chiroteuthis grimaldii*, showing heat-sensory organs as round spots on fin. The animal's tentacles are indicated by broken lines.
After Joubin

[87]

in the male dibranch, for the transfer of sperm to the female. The arm so modified is not the same in all species, being on the right side of the body in some and on the left in others. However, in most species, whether on the animal's right or left side, this arm is either the first, the third, or the fourth arm from the front. Some individuals have more than one hectocotylized arm, and the form the modification takes differs greatly: In some

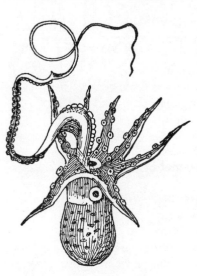

species it consists in a mere reduction (in size and number) of the suckers on the arm; in others it may be so complex that the terminal half of the arm has assumed the shape of a wormlike lash, and it is this lash which may become detached during mating and left in the female's mantle cavity (Fig. 26).

The modification of the arm in a certain species must, of course, be consistent with the method of copulation in that species. According to Dr. Gilman A. Drew, there appear to be three

Fig. 26. Male paper nautilus (*Argonauta argo*) with hectocotylized arm. After Müller

methods by which cephalopods copulate. In the first method the hectocotylized arm, charged with spermatophores (sperm capsules), is liberated in the mantle cavity of the female; in the second, the arm does not liberate any portion of itself but is so modified that it can transfer spermatophores by a mechanism within itself to the region of the oviduct, in the female's mantle cavity; and in the third, a slight modification of one arm enables the male to grasp the spermatophores as they appear at the mouth of the funnel leading from his mantle cavity and transfer them with great speed either to the mantle cavity of the female, or, in certain squids, to the membrane surrounding her mouth, known as the buccal membrane.

To understand this last method, which is that employed by the squid *Loligo pealii*, it is necessary to bear in mind

Fig. 27. Spermatophore of *Loligo pealii* completely formed, as taken from the spermatophoric sac. After Drew

that the genital duct of the male opens into his mantle cavity, the exit from which is through the funnel.

In the three genera of cephalopods in which a section of the modified arm is known to be detached and left in the mantle cavity of the female, it appears that the male can replace the detached section.

But the extraordinary feature of the reproductive mechanism of cephalopods is the spermatophore. This is a complex tubular structure, which in some species may attain a length of twenty inches. It contains a mass of sperm, a cement body for attaching this mass to the female, and an ejaculatory apparatus for extruding it (Fig. 27). Ejaculation, which in *Loligo pealii*, at least, apparently begins at the moment of extrusion of the spermatophore from the funnel, seems to require about ten seconds.

Fertilization of the egg may take place, apparently, either in the mantle cavity of the female, or, in certain species, in her buccal membrane. In *Sepia* and *Loligo*, for example, the female has a pocket in her buccal membrane in which sperm masses may be stored (if they are not deposited in her mantle cavity) while the eggs are being extruded from her funnel.

When the female squid deposits her eggs they are embedded in strings of a jellylike substance which is both soft and sticky. She attaches these strings, or racemes, to

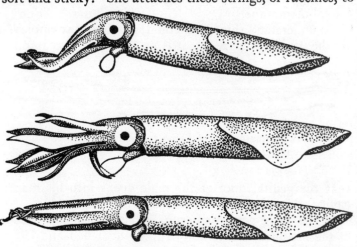

Fig. 28. Extrusion of the eggs in *Loligo pealii*. Upper, female at rest with the egg string beginning to protrude from the funnel; middle, female after she starts to swim, reaching for the egg string with dorsal arms; lower, swimming female, holding the eggs between her arms. After Drew

the submerged surface of some convenient object, a feat which she accomplishes by grasping the object with her arms and then drawing her body down tight so as to crowd the string of eggs against the object (Plate 29). Before attaching them she holds the eggs between her arms for about two minutes, molding them into a cone-shaped mass and perhaps fertilizing them from her sperm receptacle at the same time (Fig. 28). The squid always lays several clusters of eggs and prefers to attach them where others have already been attached.

The eggs of *Eledone* are inclosed in a semitransparent horny egg case, one end of which is drawn out into a string and attached to twenty-five or thirty similar egg strings (Fig. 29). One female deposits about thirty of these racemes—eight hundred eggs, more or less—during a spawning. *Eledone*, also, like *Loligo*, attaches her egg racemes to some submerged object by pressing them against it with her body.

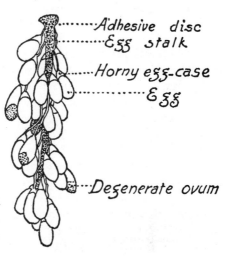

Argonauta, of course, deposits her eggs in her specially formed, shelly egg pocket, the like of which no other cephalopod possesses.

The eggs of the cephalopod differ from those of all other mollusks in their mode of development; for the young cephalopod passes through no larval stages in the egg but hatches in the form of the adult. The egg is large and heavily charged with yolk.

FIG. 29. Egg string, or raceme, of octopod *Eledone cirrosa*. After Isgrove

To what extent the female cares for her eggs during incubation is not known for most species of cephalopods. Cowdry reports that females of the species *Octopus vulgaris* living in an aquarium in Bermuda, after laying their eggs, attached them to the wall of the aquarium and then attached themselves to the wall, also, in such a position as to cover the eggs. A female rarely left her eggs until they were hatched—not even to obtain food; but she contracted her mantle from time to time and thus kept the water in circulation about her. In one instance another octopus so persistently annoyed one of the brooding females that she deliberately left her nest and killed her tormentor. When the young octopuses began to escape from the egg capsules the females became greatly excited and would dash at a man's hand inserted in the tank. At this time, also, they pulled down most of the eggs from their place of attachment and scattered them about.

It is hard to resist the conviction that the cephalopods have no rivals in the animal kingdom in the variety of startling adaptations they possess. Two more of these adaptations must be referred to before we leave the discussion of cephalopod anatomy and characteristics; namely, the capacity of dibranchs to change color and the capacity of certain species of dibranchs to emit light.

Of the Octopoda, Cowdry says that they are remarkable "in that they exhibit more vivid, complicated, and rapid color changes than do any other members of the animal kingdom" (Plate F). These alterations in color result from the movements (expansion and contraction) of the chromatophores, or pigment cells, which are distributed in the superficial layers of skin over the whole surface of the octopod's body. Scattered through the skin, also, are light-reflecting cells of a yellowish color, called iridocysts, which cause a peculiar iridescent shimmer. The fine granules of pigment in any single chromatophore are of the same color, but the many chromatophores are often colored differently. Thus it comes about that an individual of a certain cephalopod species may, by expanding all its color cells, approximate a rainbow in the arrangement and shading of its colors.

The dilation or contraction of the chromatophores is effected by muscular radial processes, which connect the color cells with the surrounding skin musculature, and these processes in turn are innervated by nerves communicating with the brain. This very elaborate mechanism in the skin of cephalopods is well calculated to produce a changing color pattern—a pattern whose patches of color are at times sharply defined and at others merge imperceptibly one into another, their various colors mingling harmoniously to form new shades, which in themselves are not constant but vary from time to time.

Now as to what causes the various color changes in dibranchs: It appears that impulses sent from the central nervous system to the chromatophores are responsible for all the color changes, though there may be simple pulsations of the chromatophores unconnected with the central nervous system. Furthermore, there is a remarkably delicate adjustment in cephalopods between the eye and the chromatophores; that is to say, the change of color in an animal to correspond with its background "depends solely upon the excitation of a reflex arc which passes from the retina through the optic nerve to the brain and thence by the various nerve trunks to the chromatophores." It has been shown that the degree of rapidity with which an octopus or squid can change color and the degree of brilliancy of the colors he assumes are commensurate with the degree of development of his eye.

Color changes apparently respond also to the dibranch's emotions; he seems to blanch when frightened and flush a dark color when angered, and such changes are powerful enough to overrule his natural impulse to assume a color which simulates his background and changes with it. The subject is a fascinating one about which much remains to be learned.

As Cowdry gives the octopods first place among animals judged by the capacity to effect vivid and rapid color changes, so Berry is inclined to believe that certain squids exhibit the highest development of the power to produce light known in the entire animal kingdom. Authentic cases of the possession of photogenic qualities in cephalopods seem to be limited to the decapods, among whom it is widespread, though actual luminescence has been observed in only a few species. This paucity of observations may be explained by the fact that most luminescent cephalopods are deep-sea dwellers and that therefore man

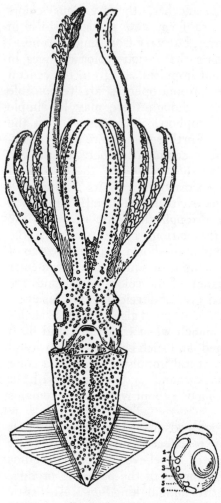

has few opportunities to observe them.

Photogenic organs may occur in almost any portion of the octopod possessing them, but are more apt to occur in the outer integument both of the arms and of the mantle sac, in the eyeball, or in the mantle cavity (Fig. 30). They are often internal and able to function only by reason of the transparency of the body tissues in a live animal.

Recent discoveries made by the Dana expeditions have revealed that *Spirula*, the curious little dibranch which is distinguished by the possession of a coiled internal shell and by the fact that its mantle forms a sucker at the posterior end, also possesses a photogenic

FIG. 30. *Abralia multihamata*. Ventral view of a female, to show luminous organs, and eyeball enlarged, to show luminous organs (1-6). After Sasaki

organ in the center of the terminal or sucker disk. It is a small beadlike organ which gives off a pale yellowish-green light. In contrast to the light which flares up and fades away again, displayed by so many other marine organisms, the *Spirula's* little lamp burns continuously. Schmidt records having seen the light showing uninterruptedly for hours together.

Incidentally, until the investigations of the Dana expeditions, the reports of which were published in 1922, a living *Spirula* was a zoological rarity. The Dana expeditions found them to be bathypelagic, occurring at depths of from 600 to 6,000 feet. Specimens range in size up to one and seven-eighths inches in length of mantle. Their preferred position seems to be head downward so that the light on the posterior end always shines upward. Apparently the gas in the spiral shell tends to keep the posterior end up.

The actual structure of the photogenic organs in cephalopods exhibits great variety, ranging from simple discharging glands and lumps of photogenic tissue to complex bull's-eye lanterns and mirrored searchlights.

As to the color and intensity of light emitted by cephalopods various opinions exist, but that this light can, in some species, be blindingly brilliant and even richly hued there seems no doubt.

FACTS AND FANCIES

Cephalopods have furnished engrossing themes for writers since the days of Aristotle. Much false information has been disseminated about them, a fact that is not to be wondered at when one considers how difficult it is to acquire accurate first-hand data on these wholly marine creatures. The legend of the chambered nautilus sailing gracefully on the surface of the sea dates back at least to Pliny. As a matter of fact the chambered nautilus lives in the tropical western Pacific, usually at depths of a hundred feet or more, and, all myths to the contrary, has never been known to sail the surface of the sea.

Not all of the many recorded stories of encounters

between men and cephalopods will bear the critical scrutiny of the scientist. Most of them are necessarily founded on the tales of seamen. But there is no doubt that octopuses and squids can be dangerous enemies. Cassell's *Natural History* contains a detailed account of an attack made by an octopus on a diver at work on the bottom of the tideway of the River Moyne, in the State of Victoria, Australia, on November 4, 1879. The diver lay flat on top of a large stone, this being the only position in which he could feel under it for a recess in which to place a charge of dynamite. Cassell's quotes the diver as follows:

My arm was scarcely down, however, before I found that it was held by something, and the action of the water was stirring up the loose clay, and therefore I could not see distinctly for a few minutes, but when it did clear away I saw, to my horror, the arm of a large octopus entwined round mine like a boa constrictor, and just then he fixed some of his suckers on the back of my hand, and the pain was intense. I felt as if my hand was being pulled to pieces, and the more I tried to take it away, the greater the pain became, and, from past experience, I knew this method would be useless. But what was I to do, lying in this position? I had the greatest difficulty in keeping my feet down, as the air rushed along the interior of my dress and inflated it, and if my feet had got uppermost I should soon have become insensible, held in such a position, and if I had given the signal to be pulled up the brute would have held on and the chances would have been that I should have had a broken arm. I had a hammer down by me but could not reach it to use it on the brute. There was a small iron bar not far from me, and with my feet I dragged this along until I could reach it with my left hand. And now the fight commenced; the more I struck him the tighter he squeezed, until my arm got quite benumbed; but after awhile I found the grip began to relax a little, but he held on until I had almost cut him to pieces, and then he relaxed his hold from the rock and I pulled him up. I can assure you I was completely exhausted, having been in that position for over twenty minutes. I brought the animal up, or rather a part of it. We laid him out and he measured over eight feet across, and I feel perfectly convinced that this fellow could have held down five or six men.

Well authenticated reports exist to prove that squids, also, have attacked men. Verrill quotes the following extract from a letter written by the Rev. M. Harvey to Dr. J. W. Dawson and later published in the Montreal *Gazette*:

Two fishermen were out in a small punt on October 26, 1873, off Portugal Cove, Conception Bay, about 9 miles from Saint John's. Observing some object floating on the water at a short distance, they rowed towards it, supposing it to be a large sail or the débris of a wreck. On reaching it one of the men struck it with his "gaff," when immediately it showed signs of life, reared a parrotlike beak, which they declare was "as big as a six-gallon keg," with which it struck the bottom of the boat violently. It then shot out from about its head two huge livid arms and began to twine them round the boat. One of the men seized a small ax and severed both arms as they lay over the gunwale of the boat; whereupon the fish moved off and ejected an immense quantity of inky fluid, which darkened the water for two or three hundred yards. The men saw it for a short time afterwards, and observed its tail in the air, which they declare was 10 feet across. They estimate the body to have been 60 feet in length, 5 feet in diameter, of the same shape and color as the common squid, and they observed that it moved in the same way as the squid, both backwards and forwards.

One of the arms which they brought ashore was unfortunately destroyed, as they were ignorant of its importance; but the clergyman of the village assures me it was 10 inches in diameter and 6 feet in length. The other arm was brought to Saint John's, but not before 6 feet of it were destroyed. Fortunately, I heard of it and took measures to have it preserved. Mr. Murray, of the geological survey, and I afterwards examined it carefully, had it photographed, and immersed in alcohol; it is now in our museum. It measured 19 feet, is of a pale-pink color, entirely cartilaginous, tough and pliant as leather, and very strong.

The literature of the past abounds in myths about sea-serpents, the basis for most of which is traceable to the giant squid. For this is the only known animal whose arms can, without distortion, be made to assume a serpentine form. Figure 31, based on the measurements of an actual specimen, shows how nearly a squid's arm may resemble a serpent. The expanded end of one of these long arms, studded with suckers, might easily be mistaken for the bearded or maned head which is usually assigned

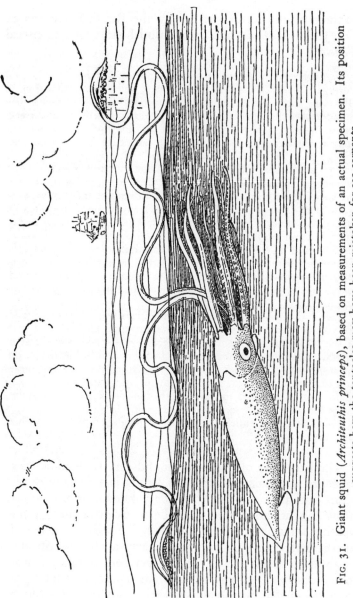

Fig. 31. Giant squid (*Architeuthis princeps*), based on measurements of an actual specimen. Its position suggests how the tentacles may have been mistaken for sea serpents

to the serpent. A momentary glimpse of such a vision at long range would suffice for the untrained mind to create a kraken, kraxen, krabben, korven, ankertrold, soe-horven, haf-gua, soe ormen, horven, aale-tust, or sea-serpent. In further support of this explanation of the origin of the sea-serpent is the very suggestive fact that the known distribution of the giant squids is coextensive with the regions from which the above-named beasts have been reported. It is also interesting to note that the size of these mystic animals has decreased with increased ocean travel and general education.

Measurements made by Verrill himself on many speci-mens of giant squids caught off the northeastern coast of North America give adequate evidence of the great size which these invertebrate monsters may attain. The largest individual he had examined up to the time of his report was fifty-five feet long over all; its tentacular arms measured thirty-five feet in length; and the length of the body from the tip of the tail to the base of the arms was twenty feet. The greatest length for tentacular arms mentioned in his table is thirty-seven feet and the greatest circumference of the body is twelve feet. The diameter of the largest sucker is given as about two and a quarter inches and the size of the largest eye opening is seven by nine inches.

My own experience with squids has given me a very high respect for their swimming powers. Until I had seen them in their native haunts I had always believed what I had been told about squids; namely, that they were old-fashioned, antiquated relics of the past, whose very method of progression—backward, instead of forward—marked them as unfit to compete with other marine animals. Well do I recall the rude awakening to which I was subjected when I tried to capture some slender loligopsoid squids in southern Philippine waters. I was on board the *Albatross* in the harbor of Jolo. The night was dark and the sea as smooth as glass. We were fishing

with the submarine light, a 16-candlepower electric bulb
inclosed in a glass globe. It should be stated here that
the sea about Jolo Harbor is one of the richest plankton-
bearing areas of water that it has been my good fortune
to visit; and where there is an abundance of this microscopic life, there, too, will be found the larger forms that
subsist upon it. A swish or two of the light and a quick
change of depth at once attracted a cloud of minute
forms; then larger animals came, attracted in part by the
light and in part by the food. The protozoans were soon
followed by worms and crustaceans, whose tangential
course would soon have carried them beyond our light
were it not that the fascination of a light causes them to
curve their path more and more and apparently renders
them unable to escape from its charm.

Thus we soon found millions of creatures drawn into a
spinning vortex about our light—the "wheel of life," as
some one has aptly termed it. New sorts kept coming:
small fish of various kinds, a school of sardines dashing
madly after the small crustaceans and worms, and still
larger and larger fish at greater distances from the light,
always preying upon the lesser circle within; now and
then even the shadowy outline of a large shark injected
itself into the distant reaches of our lamp. It was a
mad dance that this whirling, circling host of creatures
performed.

Then a new element entered: living arrows, a school of
loligopsoids shooting across our lighted field, apparently
attracted not so much by the light as by the feast before
them. They were wonderful creatures, these squids, unlike
anything else there; they shot forward and back like
shuttles, with lightning rapidity. Not only that, but they
were able to divert their course to any new direction with
equal speed. As each of them shot forward, his tentacles
would seize a small fish, and instantly he would come
to a full stop, only to dart backward like a flash at the
least sign of danger. Kill, kill, kill; they were blood-

thirsty pirates. A bite in the neck, and the fish was done for; but the sport continued, and, likely as not, one fish would be dropped and another seized and dispatched. Never before nor since have I seen anything that appeared to me more beautifully equipped for an aquatic existence than one of these squids. Frequently, very frequently, their impetuous dashes would carry them away above the surface of the sea—flying squids, the pumping of whose siphons produced a popping sound.

I had heard that the Newfoundland fishermen catch squids by using a sinker with a series of hooks attached to it. This they bob up and down in the water, attracting the squids and hooking them. We tried such a sinker on our Sulu squids, but they refused to be hooked. They would dash up to the contrivance and follow it at a safe distance, but they disdained to be caught. They would even snatch the small fish used as a bait from the hooks and make good their escape. Even the expert jiggers aboard failed to catch them. Some one had the bright idea of floating a pocket net from the beam, in which it was expected that the squids would enmesh themselves. This was tried, but we found that our squids possessed an intelligence equal to their lightning movements in the rapidity of its response to their needs. Not a single one of the thousand or more that composed the school became enmeshed. But they seemed to enjoy shooting through a hole in our seine; and it was as comical as it was wonderful to see their arrowlike forms dart through this opening—not more than eighteen inches in diameter—as swiftly as if fired from a rapid-fire machine gun. Now and then the whole school would come near the surface, pause, and then sink to a depth beyond our range of vision. Again the school would line up on the far side of our net, sink below it, and shoot up to the near side, to make an assault upon the small fish fry which attempted to escape by breaking from the water. We finally did capture a few of these dare-devil fellows; but we had to get them one by one, by watching the speedy flight of an individual near the surface and quickly casting our dip net ahead of him. The efforts of half a dozen fishermen for three nights running, however, yielded only a couple of dozen specimens.

For all their size, ferocity, and speed, cephalopods have their enemies, not the least of which is man. In many countries and since very ancient times the octopus has been considered a choice morsel. The Greeks and Romans considered it the finest food furnished by the sea. Pliny tells us that the gourmands of Rome ate every variety of octopus known in the Mediterranean. The cooks baked the creature in a sort of big pie, cutting off the arms, and filling the body with spices; and they were so careful in their preparation of the animal for cooking that they used pieces of bamboo for drawing the body, instead of iron knives, which were supposed to communicate an ill flavor to the delicious morsel. How highly the cuttle was esteemed by the Greeks is evident from a story told of Philoxenus of Syracuse, who, desiring a delicious dinner, caused an octopus of three feet spread to be prepared for the principal dish. He alone ate it, all but the head, and was taken so sick in consequence of his surfeit that a physician had to be called. On being bluntly told that his case was desperate, and that he had but a few hours to live, Philoxenus called for the head, also. When he had eaten the last bit of it he resigned himself to his fate, saying that he left nothing on the earth which seemed to him worthy of regret.

The methods employed in capturing octopuses vary with the people who pursue them. Aristotle tells us that the cuttlefish and the octopus may be caught by bait. The octopus, in fact, clings so tightly to the rocks to which he invariably attaches himself that he can not be pulled off, but holds fast even after a knife has been used to sever him from his stronghold; and yet, if you apply fleabane to the creature, he lets go his hold at the very

PLATE 31

Japanese fishermen using octopuses to recover sunken porcelain

smell of the stuff. This last procedure is still commonly practised on the Mediterranean shores, where either fleabane or the even handier drug, tobacco, serves to induce the obstinate cephalopod to surrender.

Along the Tunisian coast octopuses are taken in deep water by means of earthenware jars strung together and lowered to the bottom of the sea. After a certain number of hours the jars are raised, and frequently from eight to ten octopuses are found in each jar. Earthenware drain pipes are similarly used in shallower water. The animals are attracted by white and by smooth and bright substances, a predilection of which the native fishermen take full advantage.

Incidentally, the prosperous season for Tunisian octopus fishermen is during Lent, for then octopus is eaten in considerable quantity by devout Greek Catholics instead of the prohibited meat.

The simplest method of capture, probably, is that used by the Filipinos. I recall my first octopus hunt with them one dark night in the southern islands. Our ship, the *Albatross*, lay peacefully at anchor some half a mile off a Moro village, whose dim outline was faintly silhouetted against the sky. We had just finished our dinner when we noticed a torchlight procession from the village down the sand spit that fringed a reef. The procession soon changed from an orderly march to what, at the distance from which we viewed it, seemed some wild ceremonial dance. Our curiosity thoroughly aroused, we lowered a boat and soon joined the party. It was made up of men and boys, each clad in the conventional G-string costume and provided with a torch four to six inches in diameter and probably ten to twelve feet in length, made of segments of dried, split bamboo. Each native carried his torch on the left shoulder and held it by the left hand with the lighted end in front. The right hand was reserved for a bolo or spear. The light of these torches penetrated the shallow water and revealed the luckless octopuses, which seemed to have forsaken the secure caverns of the reef and to have gone a-hunting on the shallow flats within. They are curious creatures, and their humped-up attitude and large eyes render them rather comical at such times. But there is little time allowed for the contemplation of any one particular animal, for a native bolo or spear brings him to land to be strung promptly on a rattan string.

We secured enough specimens that night to enable us to spare some to the cook, for Ming assured us that they were "vely good." So they were—or rather, I should say, it was—for I chewed a single tentacle during the greater part of the following forenoon and relinquished it only, and that with regret, when my jaws, aching from over-exertion, refused to operate any longer.

On the island of Guam we found an entirely different method in use. Here we watched the natives fishing for the octopus on the inside of the slender reef that stretched from Cabras Island toward the steamer entrance to the beautiful Apra Bay and Harbor. The natives here tie a large, repulsive-looking holothurian to a line with a sinker attached, which is then lowered among the crevices of the reef. If it finds a cavity containing an octopus, the latter at once leaves the premises and is then easily speared by the man in the bow of the canoe. There is evidently something about the holothurian that is extremely distasteful to the octopus. It is quite a picture to see these fishermen working in the very teeth of the pounding surf with a craft so frail that one constantly wonders how they manage to keep it from being dashed to pieces.

Dr. H. M. Smith writes as follows of the manner in which the Japanese fishermen catch these animals:

The octopus or devilfish is abundant and is an important food product in Japan, although my personal opinion is that it does not appeal strongly to the American palate. The octopus is caught in various ways, one of the most interesting of which is by the use of earthenware pots, which are lowered to the bottom by means of cords;

they are entered by the octopuses, which, having insinuated themselves, are reluctant to withdraw, so that the pots may be pulled to the surface before the animals try to escape. I bring up this fishery in order to refer to a very ingenious corollary, which was first mentioned to me by a professor in the Imperial University and later verified by myself. More than a century ago a vessel laden with a very valuable cargo of porcelains from Korea destined for the imperial household was wrecked in the Inland Sea; the captain and other officers did what seems to have been a favorite amusement of the olden days; namely, they committed suicide just before the vessel sank in deep water. Recently the fishermen have been recovering pieces of this pottery, which now has an appreciated value, by tying strings to octopuses and lowering them in the vicinity of the wreck. The animals enter the vessels and retain their hold of them while being drawn to the surface. Several pieces of this porcelain which I saw were gems, seeming but little the worse for their prolonged submergence.

In western countries the principal use made of cephalopods is undoubtedly as bait. The ancient Mediterranean fishermen used to roast the fleshy parts of the cuttlefish for this purpose, but the American cod fisherman salts it.

Some years ago Simmonds wrote:

The common *Loligo* is the favorite food of the cod and is therefore itself fished for bait. One-half of all the cod taken on the banks of Newfoundland are said to be caught by it. When the vast shoals of this mollusk approach the coast, hundreds of vessels are ready to capture them, forming an extensive cuttle fishery, engaging 500 sail of French, English, and American ships. During violent gales of wind hundreds of tons of them are often thrown up together in beds on the flat beaches, the decay of which spreads an intolerable effluvium around. They must themselves be consumed in enormous numbers, for it has been estimated that a single squid will lay in one season 40,000 eggs.

The annual catch of squids is said by the United States Bureau of Fisheries to amount to about three million pounds, estimated to have a value of about $43,500. Sixty-six per cent are caught in traps in moss, chiefly about Cape Cod, though many are obtained in this manner along the coast all the way from Maine to Maryland. Considerable quantities in addition to those noted in the above statistics are obtained by American fishing vessels on the coast of Canada and Newfoundland. On our west coast squids are caught for food, being chiefly used by the Oriental element of the population. All through the South Seas, the Philippines, and Japan, as well as the adjacent mainland countries, one may see split and dried cuttlefish hung in the stores for sale. In the Mediterranean countries they are usually pickled. The cuttle bone is not only used as an adjunct to the canary's cage, but in powdered form has served as a fine polishing powder, a dentrifice, and an ingredient of medicines. The ladies of ancient days knew it also, for they were accustomed to use the burned product, known to them as pearl powder, as an aid to beauty. In later days this was even improved upon by the addition of a bit of carmine to form the so-called French rouge.

Aside from man the sperm whale is undoubtedly the worst enemy of the monstrous squids; for it is well known that parts of squids are usually to be found in the stomach of a captured whale or that he vomits them out when the whalers take him. And the marks of cephalopod suckers indelibly impressed in the skin of more than one captured whale has proved that the giant mammal does not master his victim without himself suffering pain.

SELECTED BIBLIOGRAPHY

ARNOLD, AUGUSTA F. The sea-beach at ebb tide. (A guide to the study of the seaweeds and the lower animal life found between tide marks.) New York, 1903.

COOKE, *Rev.* A. H. (and others). Molluscs and brachiopods. Vol. 3, Cambridge Natural History. New York, 1895.

FISCHER, PAUL. Manuel de Conchyliologie. Paris, 1887.

JOHNSON, MYRTLE ELIZABETH, AND SNOOK, HENRY JAMES. Seashore animals of the Pacific coast. New York, 1927. Reprinted by Dover, 1967.

KEEP, JOSIAH. West coast shells. San Francisco, 1888.

OLDROYD, IDA S. The marine shells of the west coast of North America. Vol. 1, 1924; Vol. 2, Pts. 1 and 2, 1927. Stanford University.

ROGERS, *Mrs.* JULIA ELLEN. The shell book. New York, 1908.

SIMPSON, CHARLES T. Descriptive catalogue of the Naiades. 3 vols. Detroit, 1914.

TRYON, GEORGE W., Jr. Structural and systematic conchology. 3 vols. Academy of Natural Sciences, Philadelphia, 1882, 1883, 1884.

—— and PILSBRY, HENRY A. Manual of conchology: Marines, Vols. 1–17, 1879–1898; Land mollusks, Vols. 1–27, 1885–1926.* Academy of Natural Sciences, Philadelphia.

VARIOUS AUTHORS. Proceedings: Malacological Society of London, Vols. 1–16, 1893–1925.

—— The Nautilus; Boston Society of Natural History, Vols. 1–44, 1886–1931.

INDEX

INDEX

INDEX

A CATALOGUE OF SELECTED DOVER BOOKS
IN ALL FIELDS OF INTEREST

A CATALOGUE OF SELECTED DOVER BOOKS
IN ALL FIELDS OF INTEREST

WHAT IS SCIENCE?, *N. Campbell*
The role of experiment and measurement, the function of mathematics, the nature of scientific laws, the difference between laws and theories, the limitations of science, and many similarly provocative topics are treated clearly and without technicalities by an eminent scientist. "Still an excellent introduction to scientific philosophy," H. Margenau in *Physics Today.* "A first-rate primer . . . deserves a wide audience," *Scientific American.* 192pp. 5⅜ x 8.
60043-2 Paperbound $1.25

THE NATURE OF LIGHT AND COLOUR IN THE OPEN AIR, *M. Minnaert*
Why are shadows sometimes blue, sometimes green, or other colors depending on the light and surroundings? What causes mirages? Why do multiple suns and moons appear in the sky? Professor Minnaert explains these unusual phenomena and hundreds of others in simple, easy-to-understand terms based on optical laws and the properties of light and color. No mathematics is required but artists, scientists, students, and everyone fascinated by these "tricks" of nature will find thousands of useful and amazing pieces of information. Hundreds of observational experiments are suggested which require no special equipment. 200 illustrations; 42 photos. xvi + 362pp. 5⅜ x 8.
20196-1 Paperbound $2.75

THE STRANGE STORY OF THE QUANTUM, AN ACCOUNT FOR THE GENERAL READER OF THE GROWTH OF IDEAS UNDERLYING OUR PRESENT ATOMIC KNOWLEDGE, *B. Hoffmann*
Presents lucidly and expertly, with barest amount of mathematics, the problems and theories which led to modern quantum physics. Dr. Hoffmann begins with the closing years of the 19th century, when certain trifling discrepancies were noticed, and with illuminating analogies and examples takes you through the brilliant concepts of Planck, Einstein, Pauli, Broglie, Bohr, Schroedinger, Heisenberg, Dirac, Sommerfeld, Feynman, etc. This edition includes a new, long postscript carrying the story through 1958. "Of the books attempting an account of the history and contents of our modern atomic physics which have come to my attention, this is the best," H. Margenau, Yale University, in *American Journal of Physics.* 32 tables and line illustrations. Index. 275pp. 5⅜ x 8.
20518-5 Paperbound $2.00

GREAT IDEAS OF MODERN MATHEMATICS: THEIR NATURE AND USE, *Jagjit Singh*
Reader with only high school math will understand main mathematical ideas of modern physics, astronomy, genetics, psychology, evolution, etc. better than many who use them as tools, but comprehend little of their basic structure. Author uses his wide knowledge of non-mathematical fields in brilliant exposition of differential equations, matrices, group theory, logic, statistics, problems of mathematical foundations, imaginary numbers, vectors, etc. Original publication. 2 appendixes. 2 indexes. 65 ills. 322pp. 5⅜ x 8.
20587-8 Paperbound $2.50

THE MUSIC OF THE SPHERES: THE MATERIAL UNIVERSE — FROM ATOM TO QUASAR, SIMPLY EXPLAINED, *Guy Murchie*
Vast compendium of fact, modern concept and theory, observed and calculated data, historical background guides intelligent layman through the material universe. Brilliant exposition of earth's construction, explanations for moon's craters, atmospheric components of Venus and Mars (with data from recent fly-by's), sun spots, sequences of star birth and death, neighboring galaxies, contributions of Galileo, Tycho Brahe, Kepler, etc.; and (Vol. 2) construction of the atom (describing newly discovered sigma and xi subatomic particles), theories of sound, color and light, space and time, including relativity theory, quantum theory, wave theory, probability theory, work of Newton, Maxwell, Faraday, Einstein, de Broglie, etc. "Best presentation yet offered to the intelligent general reader," *Saturday Review*. Revised (1967). Index. 319 illustrations by the author. Total of xx + 644pp. 5⅜ x 8½.
21809-0, 21810-4 Two volume set, paperbound $5.00

FOUR LECTURES ON RELATIVITY AND SPACE, *Charles Proteus Steinmetz*
Lecture series, given by great mathematician and electrical engineer, generally considered one of the best popular-level expositions of special and general relativity theories and related questions. Steinmetz translates complex mathematical reasoning into language accessible to laymen through analogy, example and comparison. Among topics covered are relativity of motion, location, time; of mass; acceleration; 4-dimensional time-space; geometry of the gravitational field; curvature and bending of space; non-Euclidean geometry. Index. 40 illustrations. x + 142pp. 5⅜ x 8½.
61771-8 Paperbound $1.50

HOW TO KNOW THE WILD FLOWERS, *Mrs. William Starr Dana*
Classic nature book that has introduced thousands to wonders of American wild flowers. Color-season principle of organization is easy to use, even by those with no botanical training, and the genial, refreshing discussions of history, folklore, uses of over 1,000 native and escape flowers, foliage plants are informative as well as fun to read. Over 170 full-page plates, collected from several editions, may be colored in to make permanent records of finds. Revised to conform with 1950 edition of Gray's Manual of Botany. xlii + 438pp. 5⅜ x 8½.
20332-8 Paperbound $2.50

MANUAL OF THE TREES OF NORTH AMERICA, *Charles Sprague Sargent*
Still unsurpassed as most comprehensive, reliable study of North American tree characteristics, precise locations and distribution. By dean of American dendrologists. Every tree native to U.S., Canada, Alaska; 185 genera, 717 species, described in detail—leaves, flowers, fruit, winterbuds, bark, wood, growth habits, etc. plus discussion of varieties and local variants, immaturity variations. Over 100 keys, including unusual 11-page analytical key to genera, aid in identification. 783 clear illustrations of flowers, fruit, leaves. An unmatched permanent reference work for all nature lovers. Second enlarged (1926) edition. Synopsis of families. Analytical key to genera. Glossary of technical terms. Index. 783 illustrations, 1 map. Total of 982pp. 5⅜ x 8.
20277-1, 20278-X Two volume set, paperbound $6.00

IT'S FUN TO MAKE THINGS FROM SCRAP MATERIALS,
Evelyn Glantz Hershoff
What use are empty spools, tin cans, bottle tops? What can be made from rubber bands, clothes pins, paper clips, and buttons? This book provide simply worded instructions and large diagrams showing you how to make cookie cutters, toy trucks, paper turkeys, Halloween masks, telephone sets aprons, linoleum block- and spatter prints — in all 399 projects! Many are easy enough for young children to figure out for themselves; some challenging enough to entertain adults; all are remarkably ingenious ways to make things from materials that cost pennies or less! Formerly "Scrap Fun for Everyone." Index. 214 illustrations. 373pp. 5⅜ x 8½.   21251-3 Paperbound $2.00

SYMBOLIC LOGIC and THE GAME OF LOGIC, *Lewis Carroll*
"Symbolic Logic" is not concerned with modern symbolic logic, but is instead a collection of over 380 problems posed with charm and imagination, using the syllogism and a fascinating diagrammatic method of drawing conclusions In "The Game of Logic" Carroll's whimsical imagination devises a logical game played with 2 diagrams and counters (included) to manipulate hundreds of tricky syllogisms. The final section, "Hit or Miss" is a lagniappe of 101 additional puzzles in the delightful Carroll manner. Until this reprint edition both of these books were rarities costing up to $15 each. Symbolic Logic: Index. xxxi + 199pp. The Game of Logic: 96pp. 2 vols. bound as one. 5⅜ x 8
20492-8 Paperbound $2.50

MATHEMATICAL PUZZLES OF SAM LOYD, PART I
selected and edited by M. Gardner
Choice puzzles by the greatest American puzzle creator and innovator. Selected from his famous collection, "Cyclopedia of Puzzles," they retain the unique style and historical flavor of the originals. There are posers based on arithmetic, algebra, probability, game theory, route tracing, topology, counter and sliding block, operations research, geometrical dissection. Includes the famous "14-15" puzzle which was a national craze, and his "Horse of a Different Color" which sold millions of copies. 117 of his most ingenious puzzles in all. 120 line drawings and diagrams. Solutions. Selected references. xx + 167pp. 5⅜ x 8.
20498-7 Paperbound $1.35

STRING FIGURES AND HOW TO MAKE THEM, *Caroline Furness Jayne*
107 string figures plus variations selected from the best primitive and modern examples developed by Navajo, Apache, pygmies of Africa, Eskimo, in Europe, Australia, China, etc. The most readily understandable, easy-to-follow book in English on perennially popular recreation. Crystal-clear exposition; step-by-step diagrams. Everyone from kindergarten children to adults looking for unusual diversion will be endlessly amused. Index. Bibliography. Introduction by A. C. Haddon. 17 full-page plates, 960 illustrations. xxiii + 401pp. 5⅜ x 8½.
20152-X Paperbound $2.50

PAPER FOLDING FOR BEGINNERS, *W. D. Murray and F. J. Rigney*
A delightful introduction to the varied and entertaining Japanese art of origami (paper folding), with a full, crystal-clear text that anticipates every difficulty; over 275 clearly labeled diagrams of all important stages in creation. You get results at each stage, since complex figures are logically developed from simpler ones. 43 different pieces are explained: sailboats, frogs, roosters, etc. 6 photographic plates. 279 diagrams. 95pp. 5⅝ x 8⅜.
20713-7 Paperbound $1.00

PRINCIPLES OF ART HISTORY,
H. Wölfflin
Analyzing such terms as "baroque," "classic," "neoclassic," "primitive,"
"picturesque," and 164 different works by artists like Botticelli, van Cleve,
Dürer, Hobbema, Holbein, Hals, Rembrandt, Titian, Brueghel, Vermeer, and
many others, the author establishes the classifications of art history and style
on a firm, concrete basis. This classic of art criticism shows what really
occurred between the 14th-century primitives and the sophistication of the
18th century in terms of basic attitudes and philosophies. "A remarkable
lesson in the art of seeing," *Sat. Rev. of Literature.* Translated from the 7th
German edition. 150 illustrations. 254pp. 6⅛ x 9¼. 20276-3 Paperbound $2.50

PRIMITIVE ART,
Franz Boas
This authoritative and exhaustive work by a great American anthropologist
covers the entire gamut of primitive art. Pottery, leatherwork, metal work,
stone work, wood, basketry, are treated in detail. Theories of primitive art,
historical depth in art history, technical virtuosity, unconscious levels of pat-
terning, symbolism, styles, literature, music, dance, etc. A must book for the
interested layman, the anthropologist, artist, handicrafter (hundreds of unusual motifs), and the historian. Over 900 illustrations (50 ceramic vessels,
12 totem poles, etc.). 376pp. 5⅜ x 8. 20025-6 Paperbound $2.50

THE GENTLEMAN AND CABINET MAKER'S DIRECTOR,
Thomas Chippendale
A reprint of the 1762 catalogue of furniture designs that went on to influence
generations of English and Colonial and Early Republic American furniture
makers. The 200 plates, most of them full-page sized, show Chippendale's
designs for French (Louis XV), Gothic, and Chinese-manner chairs, sofas,
canopy and dome beds, cornices, chamber organs, cabinets, shaving tables,
commodes, picture frames, frets, candle stands, chimney pieces, decorations, etc.
The drawings are all elegant and highly detailed; many include construction
diagrams and elevations. A supplement of 24 photographs shows surviving
pieces of original and Chippendale-style pieces of furniture. Brief biography
of Chippendale by N. I. Bienenstock, editor of *Furniture World.* Reproduced
from the 1762 edition. 200 plates, plus 19 photographic plates. vi + 249pp.
9⅛ x 12¼. 21601-2 Paperbound $4.00

AMERICAN ANTIQUE FURNITURE: A BOOK FOR AMATEURS,
Edgar G. Miller, Jr.
Standard introduction and practical guide to identification of valuable
American antique furniture. 2115 illustrations, mostly photographs taken by
the author in 148 private homes, are arranged in chronological order in extensive chapters on chairs, sofas, chests, desks, bedsteads, mirrors, tables, clocks,
and other articles. Focus is on furniture accessible to the collector, including
simpler pieces and a larger than usual coverage of Empire style. Introductory
chapters identify structural elements, characteristics of various styles, how to
avoid fakes, etc. "We are frequently asked to name some book on American
furniture that will meet the requirements of the novice collector, the beginning dealer, and . . . the general public. . . . We believe Mr. Miller's two
volumes more completely satisfy this specification than any other work,"
Antiques. Appendix. Index. Total of vi + 1106pp. 7⅞ x 10¾.
21599-7, 21600-4 Two volume set, paperbound $10.00

THE BAD CHILD'S BOOK OF BEASTS, MORE BEASTS FOR WORSE CHILDREN and A MORAL ALPHABET, *H. Belloc*
Hardly and anthology of humorous verse has appeared in the last 50 year without at least a couple of these famous nonsense verses. But one must see the entire volumes — with all the delightful original illustrations by Sir Basi Blackwood — to appreciate fully Belloc's charming and witty verses that play so subacidly on the platitudes of life and morals that beset his day — and ours A great humor classic. Three books in one. Total of 157pp. 5⅜ x 8.
20749-8 Paperbound $1.25

THE DEVIL'S DICTIONARY, *Ambrose Bierce*
Sardonic and irreverent barbs puncturing the pomposities and absurdities of American politics, business, religion, literature, and arts, by the country's greatest satirist in the classic tradition. Epigrammatic as Shaw, piercing as Swift, American as Mark Twain, Will Rogers, and Fred Allen, Bierce will always remain the favorite of a small coterie of enthusiasts, and of writers and speakers whom he supplies with "some of the most gorgeous witticisms of the English language" (H. L. Mencken). Over 1000 entries in alphabetical order. 144pp. 5⅜ x 8.
20487-1 Paperbound $1.25

THE COMPLETE NONSENSE OF EDWARD LEAR.
This is the only complete edition of this master of gentle madness available at a popular price. *A Book of Nonsense, Nonsense Songs, More Nonsense Songs and Stories* in their entirety with all the old favorites that have delighted children and adults for years. The Dong With A Luminous Nose, The Jumblies The Owl and the Pussycat, and hundreds of other bits of wonderful nonsense. 214 limericks, 3 sets of Nonsense Botany, 5 Nonsense Alphabets, 546 drawings by Lear himself, and much more. 320pp. 5⅜ x 8. 20167-8 Paperbound $1.75

THE WIT AND HUMOR OF OSCAR WILDE, *ed. by Alvin Redman*
Wilde at his most brilliant, in 1000 epigrams exposing weaknesses and hypocrisies of "civilized" society. Divided into 49 categories—sin, wealth, women, America, etc.—to aid writers, speakers. Includes excerpts from his trials, books, plays, criticism. Formerly "The Epigrams of Oscar Wilde." Introduction by Vyvyan Holland, Wilde's only living son. Introductory essay by editor. 260pp. 5⅜ x 8.
20602-5 Paperbound $1.50

A CHILD'S PRIMER OF NATURAL HISTORY, *Oliver Herford*
Scarcely an anthology of whimsy and humor has appeared in the last 50 years without a contribution from Oliver Herford. Yet the works from which these examples are drawn have been almost impossible to obtain! Here at last are Herford's improbable definitions of a menagerie of familiar and weird animals, each verse illustrated by the author's own drawings. 24 drawings in 2 colors; 24 additional drawings. vii + 95pp. 6½ x 6. 21647-0 Paperbound $1.00

THE BROWNIES: THEIR BOOK, *Palmer Cox*
The book that made the Brownies a household word. Generations of readers have enjoyed the antics, predicaments and adventures of these jovial sprites, who emerge from the forest at night to play or to come to the aid of a deserving human. Delightful illustrations by the author decorate nearly every page. 24 short verse tales with 266 illustrations. 155pp. 6⅝ x 9¼.
21265-3 Paperbound $1.50

THE PRINCIPLES OF PSYCHOLOGY,
William James
The full long-course, unabridged, of one of the great classics of Western literature and science. Wonderfully lucid descriptions of human mental activity, the stream of thought, consciousness, time perception, memory, imagination, emotions, reason, abnormal phenomena, and similar topics. Original contributions are integrated with the work of such men as Berkeley, Binet, Mills, Darwin, Hume, Kant, Royce, Schopenhauer, Spinoza, Locke, Descartes, Galton, Wundt, Lotze, Herbart, Fechner, and scores of others. All contrasting interpretations of mental phenomena are examined in detail—introspective analysis, philosophical interpretation, and experimental research. "A classic," *Journal of Consulting Psychology.* "The main lines are as valid as ever," *Psychoanalytical Quarterly.* "Standard reading . . . a classic of interpretation," *Psychiatric Quarterly.* 94 illustrations. 1408pp. 5⅜ x 8.
20381-6, 20382-4 Two volume set, paperbound $6.00

VISUAL ILLUSIONS: THEIR CAUSES, CHARACTERISTICS AND APPLICATIONS,
M. Luckiesh
"Seeing is deceiving," asserts the author of this introduction to virtually every type of optical illusion known. The text both describes and explains the principles involved in color illusions, figure-ground, distance illusions, etc. 100 photographs, drawings and diagrams prove how easy it is to fool the sense: circles that aren't round, parallel lines that seem to bend, stationary figures that seem to move as you stare at them — illustration after illustration strains our credulity at what we see. Fascinating book from many points of view, from applications for artists, in camouflage, etc. to the psychology of vision. New introduction by William Ittleson, Dept. of Psychology, Queens College. Index. Bibliography. xxi + 252pp. 5⅜ x 8½.
21530-X Paperbound $1.75

FADS AND FALLACIES IN THE NAME OF SCIENCE,
Martin Gardner
This is the standard account of various cults, quack systems, and delusions which have masqueraded as science: hollow earth fanatics. Reich and orgone sex energy, dianetics, Atlantis, multiple moons, Forteanism, flying saucers, medical fallacies like iridiagnosis, zone therapy, etc. A new chapter has been added on Bridey Murphy, psionics, and other recent manifestations in this field. This is a fair, reasoned appraisal of eccentric theory which provides excellent inoculation against cleverly masked nonsense. "Should be read by everyone, scientist and non-scientist alike," R. T. Birge, Prof. Emeritus of Physics, Univ. of California; Former President, American Physical Society. Index. x + 365pp. 5⅜ x 8.
20394-8 Paperbound $2.00

ILLUSIONS AND DELUSIONS OF THE SUPERNATURAL AND THE OCCULT,
D. H. Rawcliffe
Holds up to rational examination hundreds of persistent delusions including crystal gazing, automatic writing, table turning, mediumistic trances, mental healing, stigmata, lycanthropy, live burial, the Indian Rope Trick, spiritualism, dowsing, telepathy, clairvoyance, ghosts, ESP, etc. The author explains and exposes the mental and physical deceptions involved, making this not only an exposé of supernatural phenomena, but a valuable exposition of characteristic types of abnormal psychology. Originally titled "The Psychology of the Occult." 14 illustrations. Index. 551pp. 5⅜ x 8. 20503-7 Paperbound $3.50

FAIRY TALE COLLECTIONS, *edited by Andrew Lang*
Andrew Lang's fairy tale collections make up the richest shelf-full of traditional children's stories anywhere available. Lang supervised the translation of stories from all over the world—familiar European tales collected by Grimm, animal stories from Negro Africa, myths of primitive Australia, stories from Russia, Hungary, Iceland, Japan, and many other countries. Lang's selection of translations are unusually high; many authorities consider that the most familiar tales find their best versions in these volumes. All collections are richly decorated and illustrated by H. J. Ford and other artists.

THE BLUE FAIRY BOOK. 37 stories. 138 illustrations. ix + 390pp. 5⅜ x 8½.
21437-0 Paperbound $1.95

THE GREEN FAIRY BOOK. 42 stories. 100 illustrations. xiii + 366pp. 5⅜ x 8½. 21439-7 Paperbound $2.00

THE BROWN FAIRY BOOK. 32 stories. 50 illustrations, 8 in color. xii + 350pp. 5⅜ x 8½. 21438-9 Paperbound $1.95

THE BEST TALES OF HOFFMANN, *edited by E. F. Bleiler*
10 stories by E. T. A. Hoffmann, one of the greatest of all writers of fantasy. The tales include "The Golden Flower Pot," "Automata," "A New Year's Eve Adventure," "Nutcracker and the King of Mice," "Sand-Man," and others. Vigorous characterizations of highly eccentric personalities, remarkably imaginative situations, and intensely fast pacing has made these tales popular all over the world for 150 years. Editor's introduction. 7 drawings by Hoffmann. xxxiii + 419pp. 5⅜ x 8½. 21793-0 Paperbound $2.25

GHOST AND HORROR STORIES OF AMBROSE BIERCE,
edited by E. F. Bleiler
Morbid, eerie, horrifying tales of possessed poets, shabby aristocrats, revived corpses, and haunted malefactors. Widely acknowledged as the best of their kind between Poe and the moderns, reflecting their author's inner torment and bitter view of life. Includes "Damned Thing," "The Middle Toe of the Right Foot," "The Eyes of the Panther," "Visions of the Night," "Moxon's Master," and over a dozen others. Editor's introduction. xxii + 199pp. 5⅜ x 8½. 20767-6 Paperbound $1.50

THREE GOTHIC NOVELS, *edited by E. F. Bleiler*
Originators of the still popular Gothic novel form, influential in ushering in early 19th-century Romanticism. Horace Walpole's *Castle of Otranto*, William Beckford's *Vathek*, John Polidori's *The Vampyre*, and a *Fragment* by Lord Byron are enjoyable as exciting reading or as documents in the history of English literature. Editor's introduction. xi + 291pp. 5⅜ x 8½. 21232-7 Paperbound $2.00

BEST GHOST STORIES OF LEFANU, *edited by E. F. Bleiler*
Though admired by such critics as V. S. Pritchett, Charles Dickens and Henry James, ghost stories by the Irish novelist Joseph Sheridan LeFanu have never become as widely known as his detective fiction. About half of the 16 stories in this collection have never before been available in America. Collection includes "Carmilla" (perhaps the best vampire story ever written), "The Haunted Baronet," "The Fortunes of Sir Robert Ardagh," and the classic "Green Tea." Editor's introduction. 7 contemporary illustrations. Portrait of LeFanu. xii + 467pp. 5⅜ x 8. 20415-4 Paperbound $2.50

EASY-TO-DO ENTERTAINMENTS AND DIVERSIONS WITH COINS, CARDS, STRING, PAPER AND MATCHES, *R. M. Abraham*
Over 300 tricks, games and puzzles will provide young readers with absorbing fun. Sections on card games; paper-folding; tricks with coins, matches and pieces of string; games for the agile; toy-making from common household objects; mathematical recreations; and 50 miscellaneous pastimes. Anyone in charge of groups of youngsters, including hard-pressed parents, and in need of suggestions on how to keep children sensibly amused and quietly content will find this book indispensable. Clear, simple text, copious number of delightful line drawings and illustrative diagrams. Originally titled "Winter Nights' Entertainments." Introduction by Lord Baden Powell. 329 illustrations. v + 186pp. 5⅜ x 8½. 20921-0 Paperbound $1.25

AN INTRODUCTION TO CHESS MOVES AND TACTICS SIMPLY EXPLAINED, *Leonard Barden*
Beginner's introduction to the royal game. Names, possible moves of the pieces, definitions of essential terms, how games are won, etc. explained in 30-odd pages. With this background you'll be able to sit right down and play. Balance of book teaches strategy — openings, middle game, typical endgame play, and suggestions for improving your game. A sample game is fully analyzed. True middle-level introduction, teaching you all the essentials without oversimplifying or losing you in a maze of detail. 58 figures. 102pp. 5⅜ x 8½. 21210-6 Paperbound $1.25

LASKER'S MANUAL OF CHESS, *Dr. Emanuel Lasker*
Probably the greatest chess player of modern times, Dr. Emanuel Lasker held the world championship 28 years, independent of passing schools or fashions. This unmatched study of the game, chiefly for intermediate to skilled players, analyzes basic methods, combinations, position play, the aesthetics of chess, dozens of different openings, etc., with constant reference to great modern games. Contains a brilliant exposition of Steinitz's important theories. Introduction by Fred Reinfeld. Tables of Lasker's tournament record. 3 indices. 308 diagrams. 1 photograph. xxx + 349pp. 5⅜ x 8.20640-8Paperbound $2.50

COMBINATIONS: THE HEART OF CHESS, *Irving Chernev*
Step-by-step from simple combinations to complex, this book, by a well-known chess writer, shows you the intricacies of pins, counter-pins, knight forks, and smothered mates. Other chapters show alternate lines of play to those taken in actual championship games; boomerang combinations; classic examples of brilliant combination play by Nimzovich, Rubinstein, Tarrasch, Botvinnik, Alekhine and Capablanca. Index. 356 diagrams. ix + 245pp. 5⅜ x 8½. 21744-2 Paperbound $2.00

HOW TO SOLVE CHESS PROBLEMS, *K. S. Howard*
Full of practical suggestions for the fan or the beginner — who knows only the moves of the chessmen. Contains preliminary section and 58 two-move, 46 three-move, and 8 four-move problems composed by 27 outstanding American problem creators in the last 30 years. Explanation of all terms and exhaustive index. "Just what is wanted for the student," Brian Harley. 112 problems, solutions. vi + 171pp. 5⅜ x 8. 20748-X Paperbound $1.50

SOCIAL THOUGHT FROM LORE TO SCIENCE,
H. E. Barnes and H. Becker
An immense survey of sociological thought and ways of viewing, studying, planning, and reforming society from earliest times to the present. Includes thought on society of preliterate peoples, ancient non-Western cultures, and every great movement in Europe, America, and modern Japan. Analyzes hundreds of great thinkers: Plato, Augustine, Bodin, Vico, Montesquieu, Herder, Comte, Marx, etc. Weighs the contributions of utopians, sophists, fascists and communists; economists, jurists, philosophers, ecclesiastics, and every 19th and 20th century school of scientific sociology, anthropology, and social psychology throughout the world. Combines topical, chronological, and regional approaches, treating the evolution of social thought as a process rather than as a series of mere topics. "Impressive accuracy, competence, and discrimination . . . easily the best single survey," *Nation.* Thoroughly revised, with new material up to 1960. 2 indexes. Over 2200 bibliographical notes. Three volume set. Total of 1586pp. 5⅜ x 8.
20901-6, 20902-4, 20903-2 Three volume set, paperbound $10.50

A HISTORY OF HISTORICAL WRITING, *Harry Elmer Barnes*
Virtually the only adequate survey of the whole course of historical writing in a single volume. Surveys developments from the beginnings of historiography in the ancient Near East and the Classical World, up through the Cold War. Covers major historians in detail, shows interrelationship with cultural background, makes clear individual contributions, evaluates and estimates importance; also enormously rich upon minor authors and thinkers who are usually passed over. Packed with scholarship and learning, clear, easily written. Indispensable to every student of history. Revised and enlarged up to 1961. Index and bibliography. xv + 442pp. 5⅜ x 8½.
20104-X Paperbound $3.00

JOHANN SEBASTIAN BACH, *Philipp Spitta*
The complete and unabridged text of the definitive study of Bach. Written some 70 years ago, it is still unsurpassed for its coverage of nearly all aspects of Bach's life and work. There could hardly be a finer non-technical introduction to Bach's music than the detailed, lucid analyses which Spitta provides for hundreds of individual pieces. 26 solid pages are devoted to the B minor mass, for example, and 30 pages to the glorious St. Matthew Passion. This monumental set also includes a major analysis of the music of the 18th century: Buxtehude, Pachelbel, etc. "Unchallenged as the last word on one of the supreme geniuses of music," John Barkham, *Saturday Review Syndicate.* Total of 1819pp. Heavy cloth binding. 5⅜ x 8.
22278-0, 22279-9 Two volume set, clothbound $15.00

BEETHOVEN AND HIS NINE SYMPHONIES, *George Grove*
In this modern middle-level classic of musicology Grove not only analyzes all nine of Beethoven's symphonies very thoroughly in terms of their musical structure, but also discusses the circumstances under which they were written, Beethoven's stylistic development, and much other background material. This is an extremely rich book, yet very easily followed; it is highly recommended to anyone seriously interested in music. Over 250 musical passages. Index. viii + 407pp. 5⅜ x 8.
20334-4 Paperbound $2.50

THE TIME STREAM
John Taine
Acknowledged by many as the best SF writer of the 1920's, Taine (under the name Eric Temple Bell) was also a Professor of Mathematics of considerable renown. Reprinted here are *The Time Stream*, generally considered Taine's best, *The Greatest Game*, a biological-fiction novel, and *The Purple Sapphire*, involving a supercivilization of the past. Taine's stories tie fantastic narratives to frameworks of original and logical scientific concepts. Speculation is often profound on such questions as the nature of time, concept of entropy, cyclical universes, etc. 4 contemporary illustrations. v + 532pp. 5⅜ x 8⅜.

21180-0 Paperbound $3.00

SEVEN SCIENCE FICTION NOVELS,
H. G. Wells
Full unabridged texts of 7 science-fiction novels of the master. Ranging from biology, physics, chemistry, astronomy, to sociology and other studies, Mr. Wells extrapolates whole worlds of strange and intriguing character. "One will have to go far to match this for entertainment, excitement, and sheer pleasure . . ."*New York Times.* Contents: The Time Machine, The Island of Dr. Moreau, The First Men in the Moon, The Invisible Man, The War of the Worlds, The Food of the Gods, In The Days of the Comet. 1015pp. 5⅜ x 8.

20264-X Clothbound $5.00

28 SCIENCE FICTION STORIES OF H. G. WELLS.
Two full, unabridged novels, *Men Like Gods* and *Star Begotten,* plus 26 short stories by the master science-fiction writer of all time! Stories of space, time, invention, exploration, futuristic adventure. Partial contents: *The Country of the Blind, In the Abyss, The Crystal Egg, The Man Who Could Work Miracles, A Story of Days to Come, The Empire of the Ants, The Magic Shop, The Valley of the Spiders, A Story of the Stone Age, Under the Knife, Sea Raiders,* etc. An indispensable collection for the library of anyone interested in science fiction adventure. 928pp. 5⅜ x 8.

20265-8 Clothbound $5.00

THREE MARTIAN NOVELS,
Edgar Rice Burroughs
Complete, unabridged reprinting, in one volume, of Thuvia, Maid of Mars; Chessmen of Mars; The Master Mind of Mars. Hours of science-fiction adventure by a modern master storyteller. Reset in large clear type for easy reading. 16 illustrations by J. Allen St. John. vi + 490pp. 5⅜ x 8½.

20039-6.Paperbound $2.50

AN INTELLECTUAL AND CULTURAL HISTORY OF THE WESTERN WORLD,
Harry Elmer Barnes
Monumental 3-volume survey of intellectual development of Europe from primitive cultures to the present day. Every significant product of human intellect traced through history: art, literature, mathematics, physical sciences, medicine, music, technology, social sciences, religions, jurisprudence, education, etc. Presentation is lucid and specific, analyzing in detail specific discoveries, theories, literary works, and so on. Revised (1965) by recognized scholars in specialized fields under the direction of Prof. Barnes. Revised bibliography. Indexes. 24 illustrations. Total of xxix + 1318pp.

21275-0, 21276-9, 21277-7 Three volume set, paperbound $7.75

HEAR ME TALKIN' TO YA, *edited by Nat Shapiro and Nat Hentoff*
In their own words, Louis Armstrong, King Oliver, Fletcher Henderson, Bunk
Johnson, Bix Beiderbecke, Billy Holiday, Fats Waller, Jelly Roll Morton,
Duke Ellington, and many others comment on the origins of jazz in New
Orleans and its growth in Chicago's South Side, Kansas City's jam sessions,
Depression Harlem, and the modernism of the West Coast schools. Taken
from taped conversations, letters, magazine articles, other first-hand sources.
Editors' introduction. xvi + 429pp. 5⅜ x 8½.   21726-4 Paperbound $2.50

THE JOURNAL OF HENRY D. THOREAU
A 25-year record by the great American observer and critic, as complete a
record of a great man's inner life as is anywhere available. Thoreau's Journals
served him as raw material for his formal pieces, as a place where he could
develop his ideas, as an outlet for his interests in wild life and plants, in
writing as an art, in classics of literature, Walt Whitman and other contemporaries, in politics, slavery, individual's relation to the State, etc. The
Journals present a portrait of a remarkable man, and are an observant social
history. Unabridged republication of 1906 edition, Bradford Torrey and
Francis H. Allen, editors. Illustrations. Total of 1888pp. 8⅜ x 12¼.
                    20312-3, 20313-1 Two volume set, clothbound $30.00

A SHAKESPEARIAN GRAMMAR, *E. A. Abbott*
Basic reference to Shakespeare and his contemporaries, explaining through
thousands of quotations from Shakespeare, Jonson, Beaumont and Fletcher,
North's *Plutarch* and other sources the grammatical usage differing from the
modern. First published in 1870 and written by a scholar who spent much of
his life isolating principles of Elizabethan language, the book is unlikely ever
to be superseded. Indexes. xxiv + 511pp. 5⅜ x 8½. 21582-2 Paperbound $3.00

FOLK-LORE OF SHAKESPEARE, *T. F. Thistelton Dyer*
Classic study, drawing from Shakespeare a large body of references to supernatural beliefs, terminology of falconry and hunting, games and sports, good
luck charms, marriage customs, folk medicines, superstitions about plants,
animals, birds, argot of the underworld, sexual slang of London, proverbs,
drinking customs, weather lore, and much else. From full compilation comes
a mirror of the 17th-century popular mind. Index. ix + 526pp. 5⅜ x 8½.
                                          21614-4 Paperbound $3.25

THE NEW VARIORUM SHAKESPEARE, *edited by H. H. Furness*
By far the richest editions of the plays ever produced in any country or
language. Each volume contains complete text (usually First Folio) of the
play, all variants in Quarto and other Folio texts, editorial changes by every
major editor to Furness's own time (1900), footnotes to obscure references or
language, extensive quotes from literature of Shakespearian criticism, essays
on plot sources (often reprinting sources in full), and much more.

HAMLET, *edited by H. H. Furness*
Total of xxvi + 905pp. 5⅜ x 8½.
                    21004-9, 21005-7 Two volume set, paperbound $5.50

TWELFTH NIGHT, *edited by H. H. Furness*
Index. xxii + 434pp. 5⅜ x 8½.   21189-4 Paperbound $2.75

LA BOHEME BY GIACOMO PUCCINI,
translated and introduced by Ellen H. Bleiler
Complete handbook for the operagoer, with everything needed for full enjoyment except the musical score itself. Complete Italian libretto, with new, modern English line-by-line translation—the only libretto printing all repeats; biography of Puccini; the librettists; background to the opera, Murger's La Boheme, etc.; circumstances of composition and performances; plot summary; and pictorial section of 73 illustrations showing Puccini, famous singers and performances, etc. Large clear type for easy reading. 124pp. 5⅜ x 8½.
20404-9 Paperbound $1.50

ANTONIO STRADIVARI: HIS LIFE AND WORK (1644-1737),
W. Henry Hill, Arthur F. Hill, and Alfred E. Hill
Still the only book that really delves into life and art of the incomparable Italian craftsman, maker of the finest musical instruments in the world today. The authors, expert violin-makers themselves, discuss Stradivari's ancestry, his construction and finishing techniques, distinguished characteristics of many of his instruments and their locations. Included, too, is story of introduction of his instruments into France, England, first revelation of their supreme merit, and information on his labels, number of instruments made, prices, mystery of ingredients of his varnish, tone of pre-1684 Stradivari violin and changes between 1684 and 1690. An extremely interesting, informative account for all music lovers, from craftsman to concert-goer. Republication of original (1902) edition. New introduction by Sydney Beck, Head of Rare Book and Manuscript Collections, Music Division, New York Public Library. Analytical index by Rembert Wurlitzer. Appendixes. 68 illustrations. 30 full-page plates. 4 in color. xxvi + 315pp. 5⅜ x 8½.
20425-1 Paperbound $3.00

MUSICAL AUTOGRAPHS FROM MONTEVERDI TO HINDEMITH,
Emanuel Winternitz
For beauty, for intrinsic interest, for perspective on the composer's personality, for subtleties of phrasing, shading, emphasis indicated in the autograph but suppressed in the printed score, the mss. of musical composition are fascinating documents which repay close study in many different ways. This 2-volume work reprints facsimiles of mss. by virtually every major composer, and many minor figures—196 examples in all. A full text points out what can be learned from mss., analyzes each sample. Index. Bibliography. 18 figures. 196 plates. Total of 170pp. of text. 7⅞ x 10¾.
21312-9, 21313-7 Two volume set, paperbound $5.00

J. S. BACH,
Albert Schweitzer
One of the few great full-length studies of Bach's life and work, and the study upon which Schweitzer's renown as a musicologist rests. On first appearance (1911), revolutionized Bach performance. The only writer on Bach to be musicologist, performing musician, and student of history, theology and philosophy, Schweitzer contributes particularly full sections on history of German Protestant church music, theories on motivic pictorial representations in vocal music, and practical suggestions for performance. Translated by Ernest Newman. Indexes. 5 illustrations. 650 musical examples. Total of xix + 928pp. 5⅜ x 8½.
21631-4, 21632-2 Two volume set, paperbound $5.00

THE METHODS OF ETHICS, *Henry Sidgwick*
Propounding no organized system of its own, study subjects every major methodological approach to ethics to rigorous, objective analysis. Study discusses and relates ethical thought of Plato, Aristotle, Bentham, Clarke, Butler, Hobbes, Hume, Mill, Spencer, Kant, and dozens of others. Sidgwick retains conclusions from each system which follow from ethical premises, rejecting the faulty. Considered by many in the field to be among the most important treatises on ethical philosophy. Appendix. Index. xlvii + 528pp. 5⅜ x 8½.
21608-X Paperbound $3.00

TEUTONIC MYTHOLOGY, *Jakob Grimm*
A milestone in Western culture; the work which established on a modern basis the study of history of religions and comparative religions. 4-volume work assembles and interprets everything available on religious and folkloristic beliefs of Germanic people (including Scandinavians, Anglo-Saxons, etc.). Assembling material from such sources as Tacitus, surviving Old Norse and Icelandic texts, archeological remains, folktales, surviving superstitions, comparative traditions, linguistic analysis, etc. Grimm explores pagan deities, heroes, folklore of nature, religious practices, and every other area of pagan German belief. To this day, the unrivaled, definitive, exhaustive study. Translated by J. S. Stallybrass from 4th (1883) German edition. Indexes. Total of lxxvii + 1887pp. 5⅜ x 8½.
21602-0, 21603-9, 21604-7, 21605-5 Four volume set, paperbound $12.00

THE I CHING, *translated by James Legge*
Called "The Book of Changes" in English, this is one of the Five Classics edited by Confucius, basic and central to Chinese thought. Explains perhaps the most complex system of divination known, founded on the theory that all things happening at any one time have characteristic features which can be isolated and related. Significant in Oriental studies, in history of religions and philosophy, and also to Jungian psychoanalysis and other areas of modern European thought. Index. Appendixes. 6 plates. xxi + 448pp. 5⅜ x 8½.
21062-6 Paperbound $2.75

HISTORY OF ANCIENT PHILOSOPHY, *W. Windelband*
One of the clearest, most accurate comprehensive surveys of Greek and Roman philosophy. Discusses ancient philosophy in general, intellectual life in Greece in the 7th and 6th centuries B.C., Thales, Anaximander, Anaximenes, Heraclitus, the Eleatics, Empedocles, Anaxagoras, Leucippus, the Pythagoreans, the Sophists, Socrates, Democritus (20 pages), Plato (50 pages), Aristotle (70 pages), the Peripatetics, Stoics, Epicureans, Sceptics, Neo-platonists, Christian Apologists, etc. 2nd German edition translated by H. E. Cushman. xv + 393pp. 5⅜ x 8.
20357-3 Paperbound $3.00

THE PALACE OF PLEASURE, *William Painter*
Elizabethan versions of Italian and French novels from *The Decameron*, Cinthio, Straparola, Queen Margaret of Navarre, and other continental sources — the very work that provided Shakespeare and dozens of his contemporaries with many of their plots and sub-plots and, therefore, justly considered one of the most influential books in all English literature. It is also a book that any reader will still enjoy. Total of cviii + 1,224pp.
21691-8, 21692-6, 21693-4 Three volume set, paperbound $8.25

THE WONDERFUL WIZARD OF OZ, *L. F. Baum*
All the original W. W. Denslow illustrations in full color—as much a part of "The Wizard" as Tenniel's drawings are of "Alice in Wonderland." "The Wizard" is still America's best-loved fairy tale, in which, as the author expresses it, "The wonderment and joy are retained and the heartaches and nightmares left out." Now today's young readers can enjoy every word and wonderful picture of the original book. New introduction by Martin Gardner. A Baum bibliography. 23 full-page color plates. viii + 268pp. 5⅜ x 8.
20691-2 Paperbound $1.95

THE MARVELOUS LAND OF OZ, *L. F. Baum*
This is the equally enchanting sequel to the "Wizard," continuing the adventures of the Scarecrow and the Tin Woodman. The hero this time is a little boy named Tip, and all the delightful Oz magic is still present. This is the Oz book with the Animated Saw-Horse, the Woggle-Bug, and Jack Pumpkinhead. All the original John R. Neill illustrations, 10 in full color. 287pp. 5⅜ x 8.
20692-0 Paperbound $1.75

ALICE'S ADVENTURES UNDER GROUND, *Lewis Carroll*
The original *Alice in Wonderland*, hand-lettered and illustrated by Carroll himself, and originally presented as a Christmas gift to a child-friend. Adults as well as children will enjoy this charming volume, reproduced faithfully in this Dover edition. While the story is essentially the same, there are slight changes, and Carroll's spritely drawings present an intriguing alternative to the famous Tenniel illustrations. One of the most popular books in Dover's catalogue. Introduction by Martin Gardner. 38 illustrations. 128pp. 5⅜ x 8½.
21482-6 Paperbound $1.00

THE NURSERY "ALICE," *Lewis Carroll*
While most of us consider *Alice in Wonderland* a story for children of all ages, Carroll himself felt it was beyond younger children. He therefore provided this simplified version, illustrated with the famous Tenniel drawings enlarged and colored in delicate tints, for children aged "from Nought to Five." Dover's edition of this now rare classic is a faithful copy of the 1889 printing, including 20 illustrations by Tenniel, and front and back covers reproduced in full color. Introduction by Martin Gardner. xxiii + 67pp. 6⅛ x 9¼.
21610-1 Paperbound $1.75

THE STORY OF KING ARTHUR AND HIS KNIGHTS, *Howard Pyle*
A fast-paced, exciting retelling of the best known Arthurian legends for young readers by one of America's best story tellers and illustrators. The sword Excalibur, wooing of Guinevere, Merlin and his downfall, adventures of Sir Pellias and Gawaine, and others. The pen and ink illustrations are vividly imagined and wonderfully drawn. 41 illustrations. xviii + 313pp. 6⅛ x 9¼.
21445-1 Paperbound $2.00

Prices subject to change without notice.

Available at your book dealer or write for free catalogue to Dept. Adsci, Dover Publications, Inc., 180 Varick St., N.Y., N.Y. 10014. Dover publishes more than 150 books each year on science, elementary and advanced mathematics, biology, music, art, literary history, social sciences and other areas.